822

Winifred Holtby School
Learning Resource Centre

This book is to be returned on or before
the last date stamped below.

Ready-to-Use Activities for Teaching
Much Ado About Nothing

JOHN WILSON SWOPE

**THE CENTER FOR APPLIED
RESEARCH IN EDUCATION**
West Nyack, New York 10994

Library of Congress Cataloging-in-Publication Data

Swope, John Wilson
    Ready-to-use activities for teaching Much ado about nothing /
John Wilson Swope
        p.   cm. — (Shakespeare teacher's activities library)
    Includes bibliographical references (p.).
    ISBN 0-87628-914-6
    1. Shakespeare, William, 1564–1616.   Much ado about nothing.
    2. Shakespeare, William, 1564–1616—Study and teaching—Aids and
devices. 3. Activity programs in education.   I. Title.   II. Series: Swope,
John Wilson. Shakespeare teacher's activities library.
    PR2828.S96   1997   96-38320
    822.3'3—dc20   CIP

Printed in the United States of America

10 9 8 7 6 5 4 3 2 1

ISBN 0-87628-914-6 (P)

ATTENTION: CORPORATIONS AND SCHOOLS

The Center for Applied Research in Education books are available at quantity discounts
with bulk purchase for educational, business, or sales promotional use. For information,
please write to: Prentice Hall Career & Personal Development Special Sales, 113 Sylvan
Avenue, Englewood Cliffs, NJ 07632. Please supply: title of book, ISBN number, quantity,
how the book will be used, date needed.

**THE CENTER FOR APPLIED RESEARCH
IN EDUCATION**
West Nyack, NY 10994
A Simon & Schuster Company

On the World Wide Web at http://www.phdirect.com

Prentice Hall International (UK) Limited, *London*
Prentice Hall of Australia Pty. Limited, *Sydney*
Prentice Hall Canada, Inc., *Toronto*
Prentice Hall Hispanoamericana, S.A., *Mexico*
Prentice Hall of India Private Limited, *New Delhi*
Prentice Hall of Japan, Inc., *Tokyo*
Simon & Schuster Asia Pte. Ltd., *Singapore*
Editora Prentice Hall do Brasil, Ltda., *Rio de Janeiro*

About The Author

John Wilson Swope is an associate professor of English and English Education Coordinator at the University of Northern Iowa. In addition to his work in teacher education, he has spent eleven years teaching middle and high school English, speech, and drama. His articles and reviews have appeared in *English Journal, English Leadership Quarterly, FOCUS, The Leaflet,* and *The Virginia English Bulletin.* He is a frequent presenter at conferences sponsored by the National Council of Teachers of English and its local affiliates. His books include six ready-to-use volumes for teaching *Romeo and Juliet, Julius Caesar, Hamlet, Macbeth, A Midsummer Night's Dream,* and *Much Ado About Nothing,* all published by The Center for Applied Research in Education.

About This Resource

Much Ado About Nothing and *A Midsummer Night's Dream* are two of Shakespeare's comedies that only recently have come to join *Romeo and Juliet, Julius Caesar, Hamlet,* and *Macbeth* as choices for middle and secondary literature programs. I believe it's possible that Kenneth Branagh's recent film version of *Much Ado About Nothing* may do as much to popularize the teaching of this comedy as Franco Zefferelli's production of *Romeo and Juliet* did. Historically, the reluctance to teach comedies has always troubled me. The comedies provide insights into the foibles of human nature within all of us, rather than expose the fatal flaws and falls from position of power of noble personages. To ignore the comedies is to give our students a distorted perception as to what Shakespeare is all about: reflecting upon the human condition.

Whatever title we choose as teachers, we enjoy these works and think them important for more than just their stories. For me, Shakespeare's ability to observe human nature and convey it through language commands my attention. His characters act and interact with others in ways that I recognize around me. His poetry conveys human experience through timeless literary form.

Although we prize Shakespeare's plays, they present many problems for our students as first-time readers. As teachers, we want our students to comprehend the plot, understand the motives of the characters, appreciate the language, and decipher countless allusions—sometimes after only a single reading.

Prior to studying *Much Ado About Nothing*, students may have studied other plays, such as *Romeo and Juliet* and *Julius Caesar*. Even with this previous exposure to Shakespeare's plays, the students expect to have problems with Elizabethan language and conventions of blank verse; however, they possess the knowledge and personal experience to help them understand and appreciate the play. Teenage readers can identify with many of the situations, characters, and themes of Shakespeare's *Much Ado About Nothing*. For instance, students can empathize with Claudio's bashfulness about pursuing Hero, whom he truly loves. Students may know couples or friends, like Beatrice and Benedick, who engage in ongoing verbal barrages whatever the situation. They also endure the frequently quixotic emotions associated with teenage relationships, such as being blindly and hopelessly in love as Hero, Beatrice, Claudio, and even Benedick appear in various scenes of the play. When we help students recall, organize, and share their relevant knowledge and experience, it becomes a valuable resource for them to begin understanding, appreciating, and interpreting the play.

The multiple plots of *Much Ado About Nothing* intertwine more completely than the plots of *A Midsummer Night's Dream*. In the latter, the plot of the young lovers remains separate from the feud between Oberon and Titania. And while the mechanicals' desire to practice their version of "Pyramus and Thisby" brings them to the forest where Puck transforms Bottom, they never encounter the young lovers while in the forest. The magic remains in the forest and, once over, the characters return to the more logical realm of Athens. To me, the plots of *Much Ado About Nothing* seem as skillfully pleached as the arbor must have been in Leonato's garden. Although the verbal sparring of the love plot between Beatrice and Benedick is the play's principal distinction, the good Don Pedro must win Hero for Claudio first. However, Don John, his bastard brother and a recently subdued rebel leader, uses the lover's happiness as an opportunity for revenge. The bumbling Dogberry and Verges and the members of the watch may not always understand the villainy around them completely, but they nonetheless are able to blunder through and catch the evildoers. Then the false death of denounced Hero and Claudio's marriage to Leonato's niece who "is very like noble Hero" complicate the resolution.

As with other volumes in the ready-to-use library, materials for teaching *Much Ado About Nothing* is a collection of student-centered activities for presenting the play to first-time readers. I've designed these activities to help students recall prior knowledge and personal experience that they can relate to the play. When students have little prior knowledge or experience that they can relate to the play, I have designed activities like the plot summaries, scenarios for improvisation, or prereading vocabulary to create their knowledge.

Although students expect structure in a classroom, they tend to dislike a single routine. This resource presents choices of activities to help students make connections between their lives and Shakespeare's *Much Ado About Nothing*. The activities afford students opportunities to read, write, think, speak, and act out in response to the play.

In developing these activities, I've drawn upon research in effective teaching, reading, whole language, and English education as well as my experience as a classroom teacher. I also wish to acknowledge the help of my friends and colleagues in developing the types of activities I have used throughout the books in this series: Sue Ellen Savereide, former instructor and Language Arts chair at the Malcolm Price Laboratory School, Cedar Falls, Iowa, and Sharon Palas, former English teacher at Denver High School, Denver, Iowa.

I also wish to acknowledge my wife, Mary Jo P. Wagner, for her support and patience; my editor, Connie Kallback, for her professional wisdom; and my publisher, Win Huppuch, for his insight.

Although these activities will help get your students involved in *Much Ado About Nothing*, I don't propose that these are the only ones that work with students. As the teacher, you determine which activities the students use, and whether they are to work individually, in pairs, small groups, or as a whole class. You also need to decide whether the students will read silently, aloud, or in combination. I also encourage you to continue using the films and professional recordings of the play that have worked in the past, for both films and recordings may be used as prereading, reading, or postreading techniques. Over the four years since I began developing these materials, I've come to use a CD-ROM disk version of Shakespeare in addition to my now threadbare hardback version. The educational catalogues are full of all sorts of educational materials from videotapes to CD-ROM disks. In addition to the ideas I present here, I urge you to develop your own specific improvisations, questions, and extending activities that reflect your specific teaching objectives that best fit your district's curriculum.

John Wilson Swope

TABLE OF CONTENTS

ACT IV

ACT V

PART ONE

Suggestions to the Teacher

A Guide to Using This Resource

READING PROCESSES

In recent years, teachers have come to teach writing as a process of prewriting, writing, and rewriting. Approaching reading as a similar process of prereading, during reading, and postreading allows students to assimilate difficult texts systematically, enhancing the students' comprehension, understanding, and appreciation. As a linguistic process, effective reading involves the reader: the reader anticipates what the text may reveal, reads to confirm or contradict those goals, and then thinks about what has been read.

To guide you in using reading as a process to teach *Much Ado About Nothing*, this section will

- explain reading processes,
- establish a rationale for using a reading process approach to *Much Ado About Nothing*,
- explain the overall organization of the student activities in this resource,
- explain the function of each of the various activities in this resource.

All activities follow a reading processes model and fall into the following three major groups, with a fourth group of optional activities called *extending activities*.

Prereading activities help students assess and organize information or personal experience that relates to what they will read. These activities help students to connect their prior knowledge to the text as well as help them to establish a genuine purpose for reading it.

During-reading activities encourage students to read actively rather than passively, taking more responsibility for their own learning. Because full comprehension of a text doesn't occur immediately upon reading it the first time, students often need help to make sense of what they've just read. By structuring reading sessions and using reading, writing, speaking, listening, viewing, and critical thinking activities to foster active contemplation of the text, students can begin to explore their possible interpretations of the text.

Postreading activities help students make sense of their earlier explorations of the literature and come to an overall understanding of a work.

Extending activities allow students to apply what they've learned about the text to new situations after they've reached an understanding of the work.

RATIONALE

Reading *Much Ado About Nothing* is difficult, even for the most proficient students. As teachers, when we read the play along with our classes, we may be reading the text for the tenth or twentieth time. We may forget that our students are encountering this text for the first time. Unlike Shakespearean plays such as *Romeo and*

3

Juliet, the overall images and themes of *Much Ado About Nothing* have not been as generally assimilated into our culture. As teachers and students of literature ourselves, we have developed our appreciation , understanding, interpretations, and love of Shakespeare's plays through our repeated exposure to them. We have read, reread, contemplated, researched, discussed, listened to, and viewed performances of them. The activities in this resource apply a reading process approach to the study of *Much Ado About Nothing* and encourage students to read, reread, contemplate, discuss, listen to, and view the play as active readers and learners, enhancing their understanding, appreciation, and enjoyment of it.

This resource provides you with choices of activities to help students understand *Much Ado About Nothing*. The selection of activities depends upon the students you teach, your instructional goals, and the time you wish to devote to the study of the play. For example, a brief unit on *Much Ado About Nothing* using these materials would include

- ❧ completing one focusing activity and reviewing the plot summary for a specific scene as a prereading activity for each reading session,
- ❧ keeping either a character diary or a response journal throughout the reading of the play as a during-reading activity,
- ❧ completing one of the postreading activities for each reading session.

ORGANIZATION OF ACTIVITIES

To facilitate the planning of your unit, I've grouped the students' activities according to act. For each act, I've arranged the activities according to stage of the reading process: prereading, during-reading, postreading. (See Figure 1: Summary of Reading Process Activities for *Much Ado About Nothing* located at the end of Part One.) Extending activities, designed for use only after a complete reading of the play, follow the materials for Act V. Answer keys for quizzes and suggested answers for discussion activities are located in Appendix C.

PREREADING ACTIVITIES

The prereading activities for *Much Ado About Nothing* include focusing activities, vocabulary, and plot summaries.

Focusing Activities

All focusing activities share a common goal: to help students organize and apply relevant prior knowledge and experience to the scene they are about to read. Because they set the stage for reading, they should be brief, generally between five and ten minutes. These activities help establish a genuine purpose for reading by encouraging students to speculate about what *may* happen rather than to predict accurately what *does happen* in the play. Although several different focusing activities are available for each scene of the play, students need to complete *only one* of them: scenarios for improvisation, prereading discussion questions, speculation journal, or introducing the play with videotape.

Scenarios for Improvisation. These improvisational group activities take a few minutes for students to prepare and present but allow them to explore possible motives and actions of characters in situations that relate to a particular scene. Once they present an improvisation to the class, it becomes a common experience and a part of each person's relevant prior knowledge. A brief discussion of the improvisation will help connect the improvisation to the action of the play. After reading, the students may wish to discuss the similarities between the improvisation and what actually happened in the scene.

Prereading Discussion Questions. As an anticipatory device, these questions allow students to talk through their speculations about what they will read. The questions tend to be more effective once everyone has become familiar with a play and its characters.

Speculation Journal. This activity begins as an individual writing-to-learn activity. After students speculate for three to five minutes about what *might* happen, encourage them to share their predictions. Keep in mind that the goal is for them to use what they know about characters and motivations, to explore what logically *could* happen and not to guess correctly what *does* happen.

Introducing the Play with Videotape. Showing the opening scenes of a play before students begin reading it can be an excellent introductory focusing activity. Any visual presentation provides the students with a sense of the setting and overall action of the scene before they confront the written text. After showing the film or tape, ask the class, "What seems to be going on here?" A few minutes' discussion will help you determine if the students have a general sense of what they've seen.

Plot Summaries

Once students have completed a focusing activity, share the plot summary of the scene with them before they begin reading it. Reading the summary helps students establish the overall direction for the scene before beginning Shakespeare's verse. With the summary as a road map, students are less likely to get lost among Shakespeare's many literary allusions.

Vocabulary

The vocabulary activities allow students to expand their vocabularies through repeated exposure to words within context. The words defined in the prereading lists are the bases for both of the postreading vocabulary activities: vocabulary in context and vocabulary review quiz. Although most of the words on these lists are in common use today, Shakespeare often used the words in different contexts than contemporary speakers do. The lists provide brief definitions and synonyms as well as a sentence to illustrate the word in a context similar to the one the students will encounter in the play.

DURING-READING ACTIVITIES

Students need to read actively. When the text is as challenging as *Much Ado About Nothing*, few students can comprehend it immediately. Instead, most of them need to contemplate the text consciously to make sense of it. During-reading activities allow them to reread, write, talk, listen, view, and think about what they've just read.

Four types of activities enable students to contemplate actively what they've just read and begin to explore possible interpretations of it: *response journal, character diary, viewing scenes on videotape,* and *guides to character development.*

Response Journal

This writing-to-learn activity is based upon the work of David Bleich. The students make four types of responses either while they read or immediately upon completing the reading of a particular scene. They respond emotionally to what they're reading and try to speculate why the text provokes a particular response. Then they record and explore their own associations and experiences that relate to the text. The figurative response then draws the students back to the text, making them contemplate an important section of it. Finally, the response journal encourages students to record the questions that arise while they read, so they can address them later.

All students keep an individual response journal throughout their reading of *Much Ado About Nothing*. They use it as a means to record their reactions to what they read either while they read or immediately upon completing a reading session. For example, if students read the play aloud during class, encourage them to take the last few minutes of the period to write in their response journals. If students are to read outside of class, then also have them complete their response journals as part of the homework assignment. The writing in the response journal is exploratory in nature: it is a forum for formulating and testing hypotheses about the play, its language, and its characters; it is not a place where grammar, usage, and mechanics are an issue.

Character Diary

An alternative to the response journal, this exploratory writing-to-learn activity encourages students to read actively and to contemplate what they've read. The students summarize the action of the play, in the form of a personal diary, from the perspective of a minor character. Because no character is present for all the action of a play, the character diary requires students to provide a logical account of how their individual characters come to know the action. This paraphrasing not only improves the students' reading comprehension but affects a broad range of related language skills, "including literal recall of events, characters, main points, rhetorical features, stylistic devices and text structure" (Brown and Cambourne, 9). Like the response journal, the writing in the character diary is exploratory in nature.

Viewing a Scene on Videotape

As an optional during-reading activity, students may view and discuss several scenes immediately after having read them. For *Much Ado About Nothing*, watching a video version may help students see the wit and humor in ways that simply reading it does not. I am especially fond of Kenneth Branagh's film version with Denzel Washington, Emma Thompson, and Michael Keaton. Similarly, I've found that my students are often surprised by the broad nature of Shakespearean comedy that may not be readily apparent until seen. Because the students will already be familiar with the play's language, action, and characters, viewing the scene permits them to use the additional visual and auditory information to improve their understanding of the play's language and characters. For example, both Beatrice and Benedick fall for the same trick: they become convinced that the other is hopelessly in love as they purposely overhear their friends' conversation.

Guides to Character Development

These guides are additional, optional means to structure the students' contemplation of a play. The guides to character development and revelation include Beatrice, Benedick, Hero, and Claudio as major characters, or Don Pedro, Don John, Borachio, Leonato, Margaret, and Dogberry as minor ones.

How you use these activities depends on the specific goals for studying *Much Ado About Nothing*. For example, you can have the entire class examine how Shakespeare develops a major character by having them choose to examine Beatrice, Hero, Benedick, or Claudio. At first glance, the students may see little difference between Hero and Beatrice; however, students will quickly discover that Beatrice is independent while Hero seems more passive. Similarly, the students can examine how Shakespeare reveals minor or more static characters like Dogberry or Leonato. Have them complete these activities individually, in pairs, or in small groups.

These charts direct students first to review specific portions of the play to determine what the characters do, say, or what other characters say about them before drawing conclusions about what insight this information provides into a specific character. You will find charts for the characters with the during-reading materials for each act in which the specific character appears. No single character appears in all scenes.

POSTREADING ACTIVITIES

Postreading activities help students read, write, talk, or act their ways through the play to reach an overall understanding of it. This resource provides four types of postreading activities: *comprehension checks, critical thinking questions, language exploration,* and *vocabulary*.

Comprehension Checks

Two types of activities assess students' comprehension of the text that they've read: a multiple choice quiz and small group discussion questions.

Comprehension Check (multiple choice). The quizzes consist of five multiple-choice questions for each act. Two are factual, two are interpretative, and one is evaluative.

Small Group Discussion Questions to Check Comprehension. These questions help students assess whether they understand key issues of a play. Encourage them to discuss their answers with one another and return to the text to clarify misunderstandings through collaborative discussion in small groups.

Critical Thinking Questions

Postreading discussion questions are probably the most common activity in a literature classroom. However, questions need to do more than simply check whether the students have read a particular passage. The Critical Thinking Questions follow the model of Christenbury and Kelly and help students connect the act that they've just read with the play as a whole, to their personal experiences, and to other literary experiences. To establish the goal for the discussion, present the focus question first. Although this question is the one that students will find difficult to answer at first, present it to them and just let them think about it. Explore the related issues in the other questions and then have the students return to the focus question to connect their other responses to it.

Language Exploration

These activities allow students to return to the text and explore how Shakespeare uses language within the context of the acts of the play that they've already read. Encourage them to use these activities to review and apply concepts and to develop interpretations of specific passages. The concepts in *Much Ado About Nothing* include simile and metaphor, personification, sensory imagery, apostrophe, and symbol.

Vocabulary Activities

Vocabulary in Context. As a postreading activity, students can examine how Shakespeare uses the prereading vocabulary within a specific passage. Then the students can apply an appropriate meaning and develop an interpretation of the passage within the context of the play. Although these activities direct students to excerpts, you can encourage students to review an entire section of the particular scene to establish a more complete context.

Vocabulary Review Quizzes. These activities provide students with ways to assess their mastery of vocabulary for each act. The quiz items deliberately repeat, in modern language, the context established in the vocabulary in context activities. These quizzes are in a multiple-choice format to facilitate evaluation.

EXTENDING ACTIVITIES

Extending activities encourage students to apply what they've learned from studying *Much Ado About Nothing* to alternative situations. They may complete these activities individually or in groups. This resource includes general directions for extending activities as well as more specific directions for acting out, oral interpretation, using puppet theater, making masks, and writing assignments.

Acting Out

Through improvisations, students can work out a skit to portray a particular scene or place a familiar character in a different context.

Oral Interpretation

These activities encourage students to present scenes from the play in its original language. With the suggested scenes, students can work either individually or in pairs. The directions include steps for preparing an effective oral interpretation. Students may wish to incorporate either puppet theater or masks into their presentations.

Puppet Theater

This activity includes directions for making paper bag puppets and suggestions for two, three, or more performers for specific scenes.

Paper Plate Masks

Masks provide a way to present visual interpretations of a character. Students can do this easily by constructing simple masks from paper plates as shown. These masks, like the puppets, may also be combined with oral or dramatic presentations.

Writing Assignments

Writing tasks give students a chance to incorporate their new understanding of the play into a piece of writing. To develop these assignments, they may want to use some of their reading process activities, such as response journals or character diaries, as sources for prewriting.

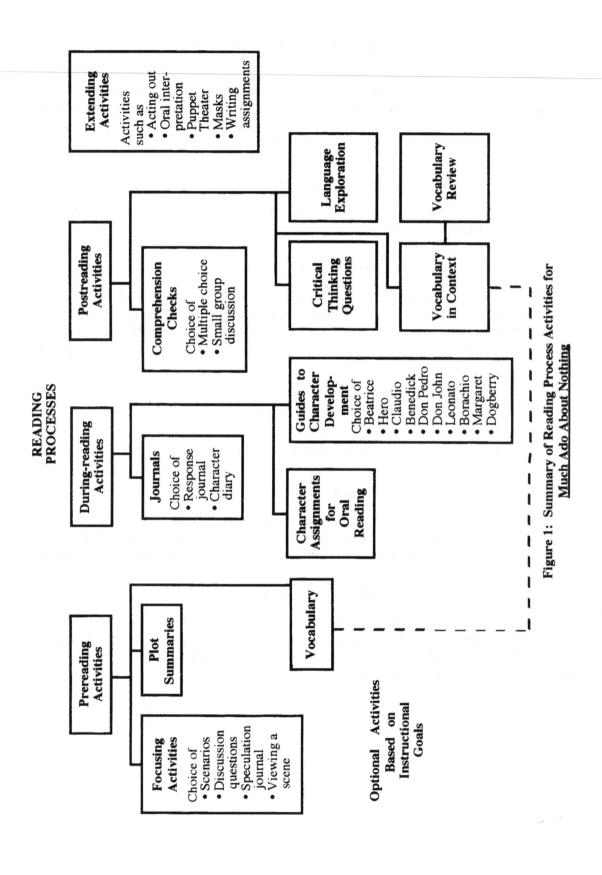

Figure 1: Summary of Reading Process Activities for _Much Ado About Nothing_

PART TWO

Ready-to-Use Materials for the Student

INTRODUCTORY MATERIALS
FOR
TEACHING SHAKESPEARE

William Shakespeare

NAME: _____ DATE: _____

William Shakespeare
April 23, 1564—April 23, 1616

William Shakespeare was the eldest son and third child of John Shakespeare and Mary Arden. His father was a maker of white leather (whittawer) and gloves (glover), and a wool dealer as well as a yeoman farmer who owned his own land. As a prosperous and respected tradesman, John Shakespeare also took part in the local government of Stratford and held several government positions including Chamberlain (town treasurer), Alderman (town councilman), and Bailiff of Stratford-upon-Avon.

During William's childhood, Stratford was a prosperous, self-governing market town. As a result, the Corporation of Stratford maintained the grammar school originally founded by the medieval Gild of the Holy Cross where historians believe young William received his early education.

The school's gildhall was also where traveling companies of actors probably performed. Records of the town suggest that William may have seen his first plays during his boyhood. The Chamberlain's accounts show that different companies of traveling players appeared and were paid from the borough's accounts on more than thirty occasions.

Town and church documents also show that William Shakespeare married Ann Hathaway when he was eighteen and she was twenty-six in 1582. They had three children, Susanna (1583) and twins Hamnet (1585–96) and Judith (1585–1662).

Shortly after his children were born, Shakespeare left Stratford and nothing is known of his life until he began acting in London in 1592. In London, he acted and served as a reviser and writer of plays. At age twenty-eight, he began to impress his contemporaries with the quality and popularity of his work. He published his first narrative poem, *Venus and Adonis*, in 1593 and *The Rape of Lucrece* the following year.

While living in London, Shakespeare acted with several companies including the Chamberlain's Men (later called the King's Men) who provided entertainment for the Royal Court. He wrote many of his plays for his own acting company. Shakespeare was also partner in several theatrical ventures including being one of the proprietors of the Globe Theater that was built just outside the city limits of London in 1599. His partners in the Globe also included famous actors of the day—Richard Burbage, Will Kempe, John Heminge, and Henry Condell. Heminge and Condell would publish the first collected editions of Shakespeare's plays, known as the First Folio, in 1623.

Although Shakespeare continued to live and work in London until 1610, he purchased New Place, one of the largest houses in Stratford, in 1597. When he retired to New Place in 1610, he was a wealthy landowner whose estate included farmland, pasture, and gardens. Making occasional visits to London until 1614, Shakespeare continued to associate with actors and playwrights for the rest of his life. While in retirement at Stratford, he surrounded himself with family and friends.

Shakespeare died at home on April 23, St. George's Day, in 1616. He was buried in the chancel of Holy Trinity Church in Stratford. He willed New Place to his elder daughter Susanna, then wife of Dr. John Hall. Shakespeare's widow probably lived there with the Halls until her death in 1623. Within a few years of the playwright's death, a monument to him was erected and placed on the north wall of Westminster Abbey in London.

An Introduction to Shakespeare's Language

Because Shakespeare wrote nearly four hundred years ago, some of the conventions that he uses in his plays present problems for modern readers. Although much of *Much Ado About Nothing* is written in prose, some of Shakespeare's lines are written in poetry. Although these lines don't usually rhyme, they do have a set rhythm (called *meter*). To achieve the meter, Shakespeare arranges words so that the syllables which are stressed or said more loudly than others fall in a regular pattern: dah DUM dah DUM dah DUM dah DUM dah DUM. For example, read the following lines from *Much Ado About Nothing* aloud:

> *Thou wilt be like a lover presently,*
> *And tire the hearer with a book of words.*

Because you are familiar with the words that Shakespeare uses here, you naturally stressed every second syllable:

> *thou WILT´ be LIKE´ a LOV´er PRES´entLY´,*
> *and TIRE´ the HEAR´er WITH´ a BOOK´ of WORDS´.*

The pattern of one unstressed syllable followed by a stressed one, dah DUM, is called an *iamb*. Each pattern is referred to as a *foot*. Because Shakespeare uses five iambic feet to a line, this pattern is known as *iambic pentameter*.

In order for Shakespeare to maintain the set meter of most lines, he often structures the lines differently from normal English speech. He may change the normal order of words so that the stressed syllables fall in the appropriate place. For example, the following translations of the former lines have no set meter:

> *PRE´sentLY´, you WILL´ be LIKE´ a LOV´er,*
> *TIR´ing your HEARer´ with a BOOK´ of WORDS´.*

As you read *Much Ado About Nothing*, be alert to which characters speak in verse and try to figure out why.

NAME: _____   DATE: _____

Conventions of Shakespeare's Staging

When we attend theatrical performances such as school plays, assembly programs, or movies in public theaters, we're accustomed to finding a seat and waiting until the lights dim, the audience quiets down, and the play or feature begins. We're also used to seeing scenery that suggests the location of the play and expect the stage lighting to help set the mood. But all this was not so in Shakespeare's time. Then people attended plays during the day, for there was no way to light the stage effectively once the sun had set. Public performance of plays in theaters was a fairly new idea at the time because the first permanent English theater had been built less than twenty years before Shakespeare began writing his plays. Although the shape of the theaters varied from square, circular, or octagon, all had a stage that was simply a raised platform in an open yard surrounded with tiers of galleries to accommodate the spectators. The stage was covered with a roof, commonly called "The Heavens." While the roof protected the actors from the weather, the attic space above could hold machinery, such as ropes and pulleys, to lower thrones or heavenly deities to the stage or to hide the sound effects of thunder, alarum bells, or cannonades. By modern standards these theaters were small. The open yard in front of the stage in one theater measured only fifty-five feet across. Up to two thousand spectators could either sit on benches in the tiers of galleries or stand in the open yard in front of the stage.

These theaters used simple stage props; chairs or tables were brought on the raised platform as needed. Actual scenery may have been suggested through dialogue or may have included minimal set pieces such as a few trees to suggest a forest, or a rock to suggest a river bank. The stages themselves had many built-in acting areas that could function in a number of ways: for instance, small inner stages with drapes which the actors used as inner rooms or raised balconies. The actors could use the inner room for the room in which Don John begins to conspire with Conrade. The columns supporting the stage roof could be great places for Benedick and Beatrice to eavesdrop on their friends' conversations about them.

The costumes were based on the contemporary clothing styles of the time. Instead of attempting any sort of accurate historical costuming, the actors wore clothes that were much like those of a character's rank. For example, Don Pedro would have been costumed as any nobleman, and Hero and Beatrice as any wealthy English merchant's daughter or ward. Occasionally, other costume pieces may have been added to suggest witches, fairies, national, or racial costumes.

During the time that Shakespeare wrote and acted, only three or four professional companies performed in theaters just outside the limits of London. These professional troupes employed only male actors. Although most of the roles in Shakespeare's plays are male, the few parts of younger female characters, such as Hero and Beatrice, for instance, were played by young boys, aged fourteen or so and apprenticed to actors. Men may have played some female roles, especially those of older, comedic women, such as Juliet's Nurse or perhaps Ursula in *Much Ado About Nothing*.

NAME: _____   DATE: _____

The Nature of Shakespeare's Comedy

If people have only studied Shakespeare's tragedies such as *Romeo and Juliet, Julius Caesar,* or *Macbeth,* they are often quite surprised to see one of his comedies and even more surprised when they laugh at what they're seeing. While the tragedies generally begin with a chaotic situation such as the erupting feud between the Capulets and the Montagues in *Romeo and Juliet* or the bloody battles of *Macbeth,* the comedies generally begin with an apparent state of order and balance. In *Much Ado About Nothing,* the play opens in Messina, on the eastern tip of Sicily in a seemingly idyllic setting. We quickly learn that the men return victorious from a war, reestablishing order. Amid this peace we learn that Beatrice and Benedick have long been verbal sparring partners, and that Claudio wishes to marry Hero but is too inexperienced to approach her himself, thus enlisting the aid of Don Pedro. We also learn that Don John means to make trouble and spoil anyone's happiness if he can. With each episode, the plot thickens and chaos erupts in the midst of a wedding. Add a couple of bumbling policemen who stumble on the confessions that can restore the balance and the play ends happily with one wedding and the promise of another.

Humor comes from several sources in *Much Ado About Nothing.* One is language and how it's used. The verbal sparring matches between Beatrice and Benedick are examples of *wit.* Another device is the use of *puns,* misusing words that sound similar to another. For example, Dogberry, like Bottom in *A Midsummer Night's Dream,* often misuses words. For example, Dogberry tells Leonato that he has "some confidence with you that decerns (rather than *concerns*) you." Finally, the action of the play is humorous. In the midst of the struggle for Claudio and Hero to be together, Don Pedro and the others trick Beatrice and Benedick into falling in love with each other. The low comic characters of Dogberry, Verges, and the members of the watch are as inept as the Keystone Cops or Laurel and Hardy in silent movies or early "talkies." They probably remind you of the slow-witted character portrayed by Jim Carrey in *Dumb and Dumber,* and their actions are often as broad as those of The Three Stooges or Charlie Chaplin. Shakespeare's comedies, like his tragedies, have elements that appeal to a broad audience, from the most to least sophisticated.

PRINCIPAL LOCATIONS FOR
MUCH ADO ABOUT NOTHING

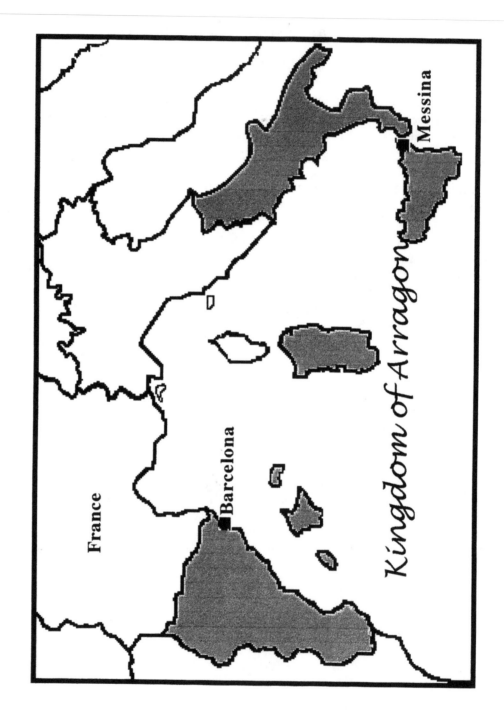

France

Barcelona

Messina

Kingdom of Arragon

ACT I

NAME: _____ DATE: _____

Focusing Activities
for
Much Ado About Nothing
Scenarios for Improvisation
Act I

Directions: Presented below are locations and situations involving characters. As your teacher directs you, but before reading an individual scene, pretend to be one of the characters and act out the situation. Don't worry about speaking like characters in Shakespeare's plays, just try to imagine how you would react to the situation and use your own language. Your teacher may give you a few minutes to discuss what you would like to do with the other performers. Your teacher will probably ask you to act out your scene for others in the class. When you finish, your teacher may ask your classmates to discuss what they've seen.

scene i. *Scene*: Outside the school commons area or gymnasium the evening of the annual Halloween costume dance.

Characters: Clay, Ben, and Pete.

Situation: Clay has fallen for the new girl at school, Hero. Clay would like to ask Hero out after the dance, but he is shy and doesn't know what to say. He asks his friend Ben what he thinks about Hero. Ben, who doesn't want to be tied down to one person yet, makes fun of Clay's situation. Pete intervenes and is sympathetic. What does Pete offer to do to help Clay?

scene ii. *Scene*: A room in Leonato's house.

Characters: Antonio, Leonato.

Situation: Antonio informs his brother that one of the servants overheard Don Pedro say that he planned to propose to Hero at the ball that evening. How does Leonato react to this news? Does he tell Hero of the situation?

scene iii. *Scene*: Another room in Leonato's house.

Characters: Don John, Conrade.

Situation: Don John is unhappy because his revolt against his brother, Don Pedro, has failed. He wants revenge. Conrade informs him that he overheard Claudio and Don Pedro's plans for winning Hero at the ball. What plans might these two make that would spoil Claudio and Hero's happiness?

23

Focusing Activities
for
Much Ado About Nothing
Small Group Discussion Questions
Act I

Directions: Before reading scenes in Act I, discuss the questions in small groups. You may want to make notes about your discussion so you can share them with classmates or refer back to them after you've read the scene.

scenes i, ii.

1. Based upon what you may have heard or seen, what do you think happens in the play, *Much Ado About Nothing*?

2. What do you think the title means?

3. How do you feel when someone "puts you down" verbally?

4. If you were shy, how might you get a date with someone you really liked?

scene iii. For what reasons would you seek revenge against someone? How might you do it?

NAME: _____   DATE: _____

Focusing Activities
for
Much Ado About Nothing
Speculation Journal
Act I

Directions: This activity is to help you become involved actively with reading the play by helping you to determine a definite purpose for reading. Before you read these scenes in Act I, take a few minutes to respond in writing to the questions below. Don't worry about correct answers here. Use your own experience, what you know, or what you may have heard about the play to speculate about what you think might happen. Sometimes, as for scenes i and ii below, you may be asked to speculate about issues that parallel the action of the play. After reading a scene, you may find that the characters reacted differently than you thought. Don't worry about these differences; just make note of them because you will have opportunities to share these differences in other activities.

scenes i, ii.

1.   Without reading the play, what does the title, *Much Ado About Nothing,* suggest to you?

2.   Why do you think some people enjoy making verbal insults that "put down" others?

3.   What problems do shy people have trying to ask persons that they like for a date?

scene iii.   What would someone have to do to you that would cause you to seek revenge? How might you accomplish it?

After reading Act I: Now that you have finished reading Act I, which of your speculations were most like the action of the characters in the play? How do you account for them? Which ones were least like the action of the play? Why do you think you speculated as you did?

Focusing Activity
for
Much Ado About Nothing
Introducing the Play with Videotape:
Act I, scene i

Directions: Before you begin reading *Much Ado About Nothing*, you will view a video version of the opening scene. Don't worry about trying to understand everything, just go for general impressions. As you watch, you may want to note questions you have to ask your teacher afterward. After viewing the scene, take a few minutes to respond to the questions below.

1.   In your own words, describe what you saw briefly. What seem to be the sources of overall conflict or problems in the play?

2.   Where does the scene take place? Which particular details help you to understand the action?

3.   What kinds of things can the director of the film or video version do in this scene that could not be done in a live production of the play on stage?

© 1997 by The Center for Applied Research in Education

Prereading Activity
for
Much Ado About Nothing
Vocabulary

Act I

Directions: Shakespeare uses the following words in Act I. The section below provides a brief definition of each word and provides a sentence to illustrate its meaning. You may wish to review the words for a particular scene immediately before reading it.

Definitions.

scene i

1. **subscribe:**   (v.) to vouch for another.
   Example: When asked to stand up for her friend, Susan willingly *subscribed* for Betty.

2. **betwixt:**   (prep.) between.
   Example: There has always been a running verbal spat *betwixt* Beatrice and Benedick.

3. **squarer:**   (n.) quarreler, fighter.
   Example: Reggie, who was a bully in elementary school, developed a reputation as a *squarer* in high school.

4. **continuer:**   (n.) one who persists or continues to behave in a particular way.
   Example: Even after the old woman recovered from her painful illness, the community viewed her as a nagging *continuer*.

5. **jade:**   (n.) a term of derision or scorn: literally, a horse of poor condition or vicious temper.
   Example: Because no one trusted Herman, they treated him as a *jade*.

6. **fetch in:**   (v.) entrap.
   Example: The confidence man used the promise of winning a large cash prize to *fetch* the old woman into his plan.

7. **temporize:**   (v.) come to terms with.

   Example: After my father's funeral, my family had to *temporize* the terms of his will.

8. **once:**   (adv.) finally, once for all, in summation.

   Example: For *once* at the end of a long trial, the prosecutor made his impassioned appeal to convict the murderer.

scene ii

9. **event:**   (n.) outcome, result, consequence.

   Example: The *event* of the vandals' actions was their sentence, to complete several hundred hours of community service.

10. **break with:**   (v.) inform.

   Example: As soon as Eric asked Kimberly to the prom, Kimberly rushed home to *break with* her mother about her good news.

NAME: _____   DATE: _____

Prereading Activity
for
Much Ado About Nothing
Plot Summaries
Act I

Directions: To help you better understand and follow *Much Ado About Nothing*, read the summary of a specific scene before you begin to read it. If you get lost during the scene, you can refer to the summary.

Act I, scene i

In the orchard before Leonato's house. Leonato, his daughter Hero, his niece Beatrice, and a Messenger. The Messenger has brought a letter to Leonato from Don Pedro, Prince of Arragon. The Prince and his retinue are returning from a victorious military engagement and are less than three leagues from Leonato's house. The Prince and his half brother, Don John, are accompanied by two gentlemen, Claudio and Benedick. The Messenger reports that the Prince has lost few men in battle. Because of Claudio's valor, Don Pedro has bestowed many honors on him although he is quite young.

Beatrice inquires whether Benedick is also returning and recounts that they have had many verbal battles previously.

The Prince and his companions arrive, greet one another, and the Prince informs all that they will stay a month. All but Claudio and Benedick exit.

Once the two men are alone, Claudio informs Benedick that he is in love with Hero and wishes to marry her. Benedick, who is disdainful of marriage and vows to remain a bachelor, fails to dissuade Claudio from pursuing Hero. Claudio admits to Don Pedro that he loves Hero but feels awkward wooing her. To help him out, Don Pedro offers to help Claudio's case with Hero at a masked ball that evening. Wearing a mask, Don Pedro will tell Hero he is Claudio and that he is in love.

Act I, scene ii

In a room of Leonato's house. Antonio has learned from a servant who overheard only a portion of Don Pedro and Claudio's conversation that Don Pedro is in love with Hero and plans to speak to her that evening at the ball. Leonato is skeptical of the news but goes to Hero to prepare her in case the Prince declares his love for her.

Act I,
scene iii

In another room of Leonato's house. Don John, who has just been defeated in a rebellion against the Prince, tells Conrade that he is discontent. Although he has been reconciled with his brother, Don John is resentful of his brother's forgiveness and desires revenge.

Borachio brings news that Claudio intends to marry Hero. Because Claudio fought so valiantly for Don Pedro and brought about Don John's defeat, Don John decides to disrupt the match.

Class Period:

CHARACTER ASSIGNMENTS FOR ORAL READING GROUPS

Much Ado About Nothing

Session 1: Act I, scenes i, ii, iii

Characters	_Group 1_	_Group 2_	_Group 3_	_Group 4_
Messenger, Conrade	___	___	___	___
Leonato	___	___	___	___
Beatrice	___	___	___	___
Hero	___	___	___	___
Don Pedro	___	___	___	___
Benedick	___	___	___	___
Don John, Antonio	___	___	___	___
Claudio, Borachio	___	___	___	___

31

NAME: _____   DATE: _____

During-Reading Activity
for
Much Ado About Nothing
Directions for Response Journal

Although we often read silently, reading is an active process. As we run our eyes across a line of text, we transform the letters and words into mental images. The words have the power to affect us in many ways. The purpose of this response journal is to help you as a reader verbalize several different types of responses immediately after you've read and to assist you in recalling the experiences of reading prior to discussing them with your classmates.

Your response journal is a place for you to react to what you read personally. This is also a place to begin piecing together your understanding of the play. Your journal is a place to think aloud on paper and not have to worry about grammatical correctness or punctuation. You may wish to do it as you read or immediately upon finishing a reading session. It won't be nearly as effective if you put it off! There are four types of responses you should make each time. None of these needs to be more than a brief paragraph, four paragraphs total.

1. *Respond emotionally*. How does the play make you feel at this point? Record your responses in a few sentences and then explore them for a few minutes, trying to figure out why you feel as you do.

2. *Make associations between ideas in the text and your personal experience*. In what situations have you felt similarly to the characters? What persons, places, ideas from your own experiences came to your mind while you were reading this portion of the play? Try to list three to five associations, but don't worry about trying to figure out why they came to mind. Just accept that they occur.

3. *Look at the language*. Which portions of Shakespeare's language attracts your attention? These might be individual words, phrases, lines, scenes, or images. Make note of whatever feature(s) draw your attention. Speculate for a few minutes about what you think these might mean.

4. *Record any questions or problems*. Make note of any portion of the play, its language, or events that seem to cause you problems. Write down any questions that occur to you as you read.

© 1997 by The Center for Applied Research in Education

Here's a sample journal for Act I, scene i:

1. Beatrice really does have some mouth on her. I wonder how her feud with Benedick got started. They both seem to enjoy putting down the other. I wonder, is there something more to the relationship than either character is willing to admit?

2. The scene between Beatrice and Benedick reminds me a great deal of the first meeting of Katherine and Petruchio in *The Taming of the Shrew*. The tone of this scene suggests friendly banter, put downs among friends. The shyness of Claudio and having someone else win Hero for him seems like an old device: it's the same in *Cyrano de Bergerac* and the modern movie version, *Roxanne*, with Steve Martin.

3. Benedick and Beatrice really love to play with language. Consider Benedick's assessment of Hero: "she's too low for a high praise, too brown for a fair praise, and too little for a great praise."

4. Apparently there's been some sort of war? Does it involve some sort of rebellion by Don John?

During-Reading Activity
for
Much Ado About Nothing
Response Journal

Directions: Use the spaces below to record your responses to the acts and scenes of *Much Ado About Nothing* that you've just finished reading. Respond in all four ways and take a few additional minutes to explore why you think you responded as you did.

Response Journal for Act ___, scene ____ to Act ____, scene ___.

1. How does the play make you feel at this point? Record your emotional response(s) in a few sentences and then explore them for a few minutes, trying to figure out why you feel as you do.

2. In what situations have you felt similarly to the characters? What persons, places, or ideas from your own experiences came to your mind while you were reading this portion of the play? Try to list at least three associations, but don't worry about trying to figure out why they came to mind. Just accept that they occur.

    a.

    b.

    c.

3. Which portions of Shakespeare's language attracts your attention? These might be individual words, phrases, lines, scenes, or images. Make note of the features that draw your attention. Speculate for a few minutes about what you think these might mean.

4. Make note of any portion of the play, its language, or events that cause you problems. Note any questions that you might ask.

During-Reading Activity
for
Much Ado About Nothing
Directions for Character Diary

As you read *Much Ado About Nothing*, you will find that the events of the play affect the lives of many characters. To give you an opportunity to explore the reactions of other characters, pretend to be one of the characters listed below. For this assignment, you will keep the personal diary of a single character for the time during which the play takes place.

Select one of the following characters for your diary:

Hero	Claudio
Benedick	Beatrice
Don Pedro	Don John
Dogberry	The Sexton
Margaret	Ursula
Leonato	Borachio

In your diary, summarize the events of the act and provide an explanation for how your character may have heard of them, if the character was not involved with the events directly, and react as your character would. For example, Borachio doesn't formally appear until Act I, scene iii. Because he has been loyal to Don John in the past, he probably accompanied all the men when they entered. However, as we learn later, he willingly helps Don John seek whatever revenge he can against Don Pedro and Claudio.

Evening of the arrival at Leonato's Palace

I noticed when we were greeted by the Governor and his family that everyone nearly ignored my lord, Don John. Instead they all fell all over themselves to be gracious to his brother, Don Pedro. Seems that Claudio is in love with Leonato's daughter, Hero. But he's too shy to approach her himself, so Don Pedro will do it at the ball tonight. Perhaps I can help my Lord gain some revenge through this.

The action of *Much Ado About Nothing* takes during a few days in Messina, primarily in and around Leonato's villa.

Acts and Scenes	**Time and Place**
Act I, scene i:	A summer day in front of Leonato's house in Messina, Sicily.
Act I, scene ii:	A short while later in a room of Leonato's house.
Act I, scene iii:	Meanwhile in another room of Leonato's house.
Act II, scene i:	That evening in the banquet hall of Leonato's house.
Act II, scene ii:	The same hall, after the ball.
Act II, scene iii:	Late afternoon a day or two later, Leonato's garden.
Act III, scene i:	The afternoon before Hero and Claudio's wedding, Leonato's garden.
Act III, scene ii:	The same afternoon in a room of Leonato's house.
Act III, scene iii:	That evening before Claudio and Hero's wedding.
Act III, scene iv:	The morning of the wedding, Hero's room.
Act III, scene v:	The hall in Leonato's house, the morning of the wedding.
Act IV, scene i:	The church, the day of the wedding.
Act IV, scene ii:	The local jail, the afternoon of the wedding.
Act V, scene i:	A street in front of Leonato's house, that afternoon.
Act V, scene ii:	The same afternoon, Leonato's garden.
Act V, scene iii:	The churchyard before Leonato's family tomb, that night.
Act V, scene iv:	The church the next morning.

During-Reading Activity
for
Much Ado About Nothing
Character Diary 1
Act I, scenes i, ii, iii

Directions: Use the space below to record your character's reactions to the events of the three scenes in Act I of *Much Ado About Nothing*. Remember to include a summary of events, explain how your character learned of them, and give your character's reactions to them. Because this act has three scenes, you may wish to record your character's entries as you read each scene. If you need additional room, use the back of this sheet.

The Personal Diary of

_____
(character's name)

Messina

In front of Leonato's house on a summer day

_____
_____
_____

A short while later in a room of Leonato's house (scene ii)

_____
_____
_____

Meanwhile in another room of Leonato's house (scene iii)

_____
_____
_____

© 1997 by The Center for Applied Research in Education

NAME: _____   DATE: _____

During-Reading Activity
for
Much Ado About Nothing
Viewing Act I, scene i
Don Pedro and His Party Arrive at Leonato's House

Directions: After you've read this scene, viewing a film or video version may help you better understand how the text translates into the characters' actions. Although you may want to keep your copy of the play handy, don't be surprised if the actors' script varies from yours. Film scripts often delete or reorder the lines in the play. You many want to note questions you need to ask your teacher afterward. After viewing the scene, take a few minutes to respond to the questions below.

1.   What do the costumes and the set representing Leonato's house tell you about the time and place of the play?

2.   How do the attitudes of the members of Leonato's household differ toward Don Pedro and Don John?

3.   How does Claudio feel about Hero and she about him?

4.   How do the actors' facial expressions, tones of voice, and gestures enhance Shakespeare's lines?

NAME: _____   DATE: _____

During-Reading Activity
for
Much Ado About Nothing
Guide to Character Development: Beatrice
Act I

Shakespeare reveals his characters in four ways:

- ❧ through what the characters say to other characters in dialogue;
- ❧ through what the characters reveal about their thoughts through long speeches to the audience called *soliloquies*;
- ❧ through what other characters say about them;
- ❧ through what they do, their actions.

As you read the play, examine the following scenes for what they reveal about Beatrice's character and fill in the chart briefly using your own words. If you need more room, use the back of the page.

Scene	What Beatrice says, does, or what others say about her	What this reveals about Beatrice's character
Act I, scene i Beatrice calls Benedick "Signior Mountanto" and assails Benedick's character prior to Benedick's arrival		
Act I, scene i Beatrice compares Benedick to a pestilence		
Act I, scene i Beatrice and Benedick engage in a verbal sparring match		

NAME: _____   DATE: _____

During-Reading Activity
for
Much Ado About Nothing
Guide to Character Development: Benedick
Act I

Shakespeare reveals his characters in four ways:

- through what the characters say to other characters in dialogue;
- through what the characters reveal about their thoughts through long speeches to the audience called *soliloquies*;
- through what other characters say about them;
- through what they do, their actions.

As you read the play, examine the following scenes for what they reveal about Benedick's character and fill in the chart briefly using your own words. If you need more room, use the back of the page.

Scene	*What Benedick says, does, or what others say about him*	*What this reveals about Benedick's character*
Act I, scene i Beatrice calls Benedick "Signior Mountanto" and assails Benedick's character prior to Benedick's arrival		
Act I, scene i Benedick and Beatrice engage in a verbal sparring match		
Act I, scene i Benedick's description of Hero to Claudio		
Act I, scene i Benedick disdains marriage to Claudio and Don Pedro		

During-Reading Activity
for
Much Ado About Nothing
Guide to Character Development: Claudio
Act I

Shakespeare reveals his characters in four ways:

- through what the characters say to other characters in dialogue;
- through what the characters reveal about their thoughts through long speeches to the audience called *soliloquies*;
- through what other characters say about them;
- through what they do, their actions.

As you read the play, examine the following scenes for what they reveal about Claudio's character and fill in the chart briefly using your own words. If you need more room, use the back of the page.

Scene	What Claudio says, does, or what others say about him	What this reveals about Claudio's character
Act I, scene i Messenger describes Claudio as "right noble Claudio"		
Act I, scene i Claudio asks Benedick's opinion of Hero		
Act I, scene i Claudio confesses to Don Pedro that he is too shy to court Hero		

NAME: _____   DATE: _____

During-Reading Activity
for
Much Ado About Nothing
Guide to Character Development: Don Pedro
Act I

Shakespeare reveals his characters in four ways:

- through what the characters say to other characters in dialogue;
- through what the characters reveal about their thoughts through long speeches to the audience called *soliloquies*;
- through what other characters say about them;
- through what they do, their actions.

As you read the play, examine the following scenes for what they reveal about Don Pedro's character and fill in the chart briefly using your own words. If you need more room, use the back of the page.

Scene	What Don Pedro says, does, or what others say about him	What this reveals about Don Pedro's character
Act I, scene i Don Pedro has reconciled with Don John for the rebellion		
Act I, scene i Don Pedro agrees to court Hero in Claudio's name		

43

During-Reading Activity
for
Much Ado About Nothing
Guide to Character Development: Leonato
Act I

Shakespeare reveals his characters in four ways:

- through what the characters say to other characters in dialogue;
- through what the characters reveal about their thoughts through long speeches to the audience called *soliloquies*;
- through what other characters say about them;
- through what they do, their actions.

As you read the play, examine the following scenes for what they reveal about Leonato's character and fill in the chart briefly using your own words. If you need more room, use the back of the page.

Scene	What Leonato says, does, or what others say about him	What this reveals about Leonato's character
Act I, scene i Leonato welcomes Don Pedro and his retinue into his home		
Act I, scene i Leonato also welcomes Don John		
Act I, scene ii Leonato tends to discount Antonio's news that Don Pedro wishes to marry Hero		

During-Reading Activity
for
Much Ado About Nothing
Guide to Character Development: Don John
Act I

Shakespeare reveals his characters in four ways:

- through what the characters say to other characters in dialogue;
- through what the characters reveal about their thoughts through long speeches to the audience called *soliloquies*;
- through what other characters say about them;
- through what they do, their actions.

As you read the play, examine the following scenes for what they reveal about Don John's character and fill in the chart briefly using your own words. If you need more room, use the back of the page.

Scene	What Don John says, does, or what others say about him	What this reveals about Don John's character
Act I, scene i Don John thanks Leonato for his greeting and hospitality		
Act I, scene iii Don John describes himself to Conrade and reveals his desire to make mischief for Don Pedro		
Act I, scene iii Borachio tells Don John of the intended marriage between Claudio and Hero		

During-Reading Activity
for
Much Ado About Nothing
Guide to Character Development: Borachio
Act I

Shakespeare reveals his characters in four ways:

- ❧ through what the characters say to other characters in dialogue;
- ❧ through what the characters reveal about their thoughts through long speeches to the audience called *soliloquies*;
- ❧ through what other characters say about them;
- ❧ through what they do, their actions.

As you read the play, examine the following scene for what it reveals about Borachio's character and fill in the chart briefly using your own words. If you need more room, use the back of the page.

Scene	What Borachio says, does, or what others say about him	What this reveals about Borachio's character
Act I, scene iii Borachio tells Don John of the intended marriage between Claudio and Hero		

NAME: _____   DATE: _____

Postreading Activity
for
Much Ado About Nothing
Comprehension Check
Act I

Directions: After you've read all of Act I, use the following questions to check how well you've understood what you've read. For each question, select the most appropriate answer from the choices listed below it. Place the letter corresponding to your answer in the space to the left of the item number.

_____1.   Before Benedick enters, we know that Beatrice doesn't like him because

A. she says that she hates him.
B. she repeatedly belittles his character.
C. she reads a letter he has sent with the messenger.
D. she offers a reward to kill him.
E. she puts a curse on him.

_____2.   Because Claudio is too shy to woo Hero himself,

A. he decides to give up.
B. he asks for help from Don John.
C. he agrees to let Don Pedro woo her.
D. he gives his claim to Don Pedro.
E. he asks Benedick to intercede.

_____3.   Benedick doesn't give Claudio a straight answer about his thoughts of Hero because

A. Benedick disdains the whole idea of marriage.
B. Benedick is secretly in love with Hero.
C. Benedick has secretly married Beatrice.
D. Benedick is already engaged to Hero.
E. Benedick has promised to become a monk if he survives the war.

47

_____4.   Antonio tells Leonato that Don Pedro wishes to marry Hero because

  A. Don Pedro has already spoken to Antonio about it.
  B. one of the servants overheard a conversation and reported it to Antonio.
  C. Antonio needs to be connected to the Prince's household.
  D. Antonio doesn't have any children of his own.
  E. Antonio likes to cause mischief.

_____5.   Don John wants revenge upon Don Pedro for all the following reasons except

  A. Don Pedro has recently defeated him in battle.
  B. Don Pedro has forgiven him.
  C. Don John is a villain.
  D. Don John is Don Pedro's half-brother.
  E. Don John is insane.

NAME: _____   DATE: _____

Postreading Activity
for
Much Ado About Nothing
Small Group Discussion to Check Comprehension
Act I

Directions: After you've read all of Act I, discuss each of the following questions in small groups briefly. Use the space below each question to note points you may wish to share later. If you need more room, use the back of the page.

1. Why does Beatrice belittle Benedick even before he arrives?

2. Why is Claudio willing to let Don Pedro woo Hero for him?

3. Why is Leonato skeptical of his brother's news that Don Pedro plans to marry Hero?

4. Why is Don John so willing to seek revenge upon Don Pedro?

Postreading Activity
for
Much Ado About Nothing
Critical Thinking Questions
Act I

Directions: To help you develop your understanding of Act I, as your teacher directs you, take time to think about and discuss these questions. The first question is the focus question and is the point of the discussion. Don't be concerned that you may not be able to answer this question at first. Proceed to the exploration questions and then return to the focus question. Select passages to support your views.

Focus Question.   If you were Benedick or Beatrice, why would you be willing to see your opponent again?

Exploration Questions.

1. What contradictions do you notice between the characters and actions of Benedick and Beatrice?

2. What sort of humor do you find funny?

3. In other works of literature, which male and female characters feud?

4. What do you find funny about the characters or actions of Beatrice, Benedick, or Claudio?

5. In what ways is the comedy in *Much Ado About Nothing* similar or different from the situation comedies aired on television?

6. Which characters, situations, or actions in other works of literature do you find funny? Select passages for these activities to support your views.

Postreading Activity
for
Much Ado About Nothing
Language Exploration
Figurative Language: Simile and Metaphor
Act I

As other poets and playwrights do, Shakespeare also explores abstract ideas like revenge, personal honor, and sacrificing personal goals for public ones in his plays. He often connects abstract ideas with concrete examples through figurative language. Although we rarely mean figurative language literally, it does help us express our ideas more vividly. Two common literary devices associated with figurative language are *simile* and *metaphor*.

A simile compares two different terms using *like* or *as*. In daily speech we often use similes like these:

&

Sam is as <u>hungry as a bear</u>.
Angel runs <u>like the wind</u>.

&

At the end of Act I, scene i, Benedick assures Claudio he can keep the secret that Claudio loves Hero, using the following simile:

&

<u>*I can be secret as a dumb man*</u>; *I would have you think so;*
but, on my allegiance, mark you this, on my allegiance.

&

Similarly, Don Pedro assures Claudio later:

&

<u>*Thou*</u> *wilt be <u>like a lover</u> presently,*
And tire the hearer with a book of words.

&

Another way to compare two different terms is to use a metaphor. Unlike a simile, a metaphor makes a comparison directly without using *like* or *as*. As metaphors, the previous examples look like this:

&

Sam is a real bear when he's hungry.
Angel breezed across the finish line.

&

In Act I, scene iii of *Much Ado About Nothing*, Don John, whose rebellion has failed against his brother, uses a metaphor to characterize his villainous nature: better to be a thorn in a hedge than a rose in a tended garden:

&

I had rather be a canker in a hedge than a rose in his grace,

&

Directions: The following passages contain examples of simile and metaphor. Working in pairs, small groups, or as your teacher directs, identify the comparisons and then review each passage within the context of the play to develop an interpretation of the passage. You may wish to review the quotations within the fuller context of the particular speech.

1. Messenger describing Claudio's valor in the recent battle for Don Pedro (Act I, scene i):

&

He hath borne himself beyond the promise of his age, doing,
in the figure of a lamb, the feats of a lion.

&

2. Beatrice describing Benedick's character (Act I, scene i):

&

he wears his faith but as the fashion of his hat; it ever
changes with the next block.

&

© 1997 by The Center for Applied Research in Education

3. Beatrice learning that Benedick's new companion is Claudio (Act I, scene i):

   ❧

   O Lord, he will hang upon him like a disease: he is sooner
   caught than the pestilence, and the taker runs presently mad.

   ❧

4. Beatrice posing a comic remedy for Claudio's disease (Act I, scene i):

   ❧

   God help the noble Claudio! If he have caught the Benedick,
   it will cost him a thousand pound ere a' be cured.

   ❧

5. Beatrice responding to Benedick saying he loves no woman (Act I, scene i):

   ❧

   I had rather hear my dog bark at a crow, than a man swear
   he loves me.

   ❧

6. Claudio's response to Benedick's question that Claudio wishes to buy Hero (Act I, scene i):

   ❧

   Can the world buy such a jewel?

   ❧

7. Benedick comparing the beauty of Beatrice to Hero (Act I, scene i):

   ❧

   There's her cousin, an she were not possessed with a fury,
   exceeds her as much in beauty the first of May doth the last of
   December.

   ❧

8. Benedick disdaining marriage to Claudio (Act I, scene i):

&

Go to, i' faith; an thou wilt needs thrust thy neck into a
yoke, wear the print of it and sigh away Sundays.

&

9. Benedick telling Don Pedro and Claudio what to do if ever Benedick should marry (Act I, scene i):

&

If I do, hang me in a bottle like a cat and shoot at me; and
he that hits me, let him be clapped on the shoulder, and called
Adam.

&

10. Claudio confessing to Don Pedro that his feelings for Hero have changed since returning from war (Act I, scene i):

&

But now I am return'd and that war-thoughts
Have left their places vacant, in their rooms
Come thronging soft and delicate desires,

&

© 1997 by The Center for Applied Research in Education

NAME: _____   DATE: _____

Postreading Activity
for
Much Ado About Nothing
Vocabulary in Context
Act I

Directions: In each of the passages below you will find one of the words from the prereading vocabulary list for Act I. Review the definitions given in the prereading vocabulary. Working individually, in pairs, or in small groups as your teacher directs, examine each of the underlined words in the following passages from Act I. For each word, use the appropriate meaning and develop a brief interpretation of the passage within the context of the play.

1. Beatrice complaining scornfully about Benedick's return from war with the Prince and Claudio (scene i):

   ❧

   He set up his bills here in Messina and challenged Cupid at
   the flight; and my uncle's fool, reading the challenge, <u>subscribed</u>
   for Cupid, and challenged him at the bird-bolt.

   ❧

2. Leonato explaining to the messenger and others of the running battle of words between Beatrice and Benedick (scene i):

   ❧

   You must not, sir, mistake my niece. There is a kind of
   merry war <u>betwixt</u> Signior Benedick and her: they never meet
   but there's a skirmish of wit between them.

   ❧

3. Beatrice inquiring about Benedick's most recently acquired constant friend and companion (scene i):

   ❧

   No; an he were, I would burn my study. But, I pray you,
   who is his companion? Is there no young <u>squarer</u> now that
   will make a voyage with him to the devil?

   ❧

4.   Benedick bringing about an end to the trading of insults with Beatrice (scene i):

&

I would my horse had the speed of your tongue, and so good
a <u>continuer</u>. But keep your way, i' God's name; I have done.

&

5.   Beatrice complaining of how Benedick ends their battle of words (scene i):

&

You always end with a <u>jade's</u> trick: I know you of old.

&

6.   Claudio replying to Don Pedro's acknowledgment that Hero is a woman worthy of Claudio as a husband (scene i):

&

You speak this to <u>fetch</u> me in, my lord.

&

7.   Claudio and Don Pedro concluding their jesting where Benedick scorns the prospect that he should ever marry (scene i):

&

Benedick: The savage bull may; but if ever the sensible
Benedick bear it, pluck off the bull's horns and set them in my
forehead: and let me be vilely painted, and in such great letters
as they write 'Here is good horse to hire,' let them signify
under my sign 'Here you may see Benedick the married man.'
Claudio: If this should ever happen, thou wouldst be horn-
mad.
Don Pedro: Nay, if Cupid have not spent all his quiver in
Venice, thou wilt quake for this shortly.
Benedick: I look for an earthquake too, then.
Don Pedro: Well, you <u>temporize</u> with the hours. In the
meantime, good Signior Benedick, repair to Leonato's: com-
mend me to him and tell him I will not fail him at supper; for
indeed he hath made great preparation.

&

8. Don Pedro promising Claudio to speak to Hero in Claudio's name (scene i):

    What need the bridge much broader than the flood!
    The fairest grant is the necessity.
    Look, what will serve is fit: 'tis <u>once</u>, thou lovest,
    And I will fit thee with the remedy.
    I know we shall have revelling to-night;
    I will assume thy part in some disguise
    And tell fair Hero I am Claudio;
    And in her bosom I'll unclasp my heart
    And take her hearing prisoner with the force
    And strong encounter of my amorous tale:

9. Antonio informing Leonato that one of the servants has overheard part of Don Pedro and Claudio's conversation about speaking to Hero (scene ii):

    As the <u>event</u> stamps them: but they have a good cover; they
    show well outward.

10. Antonio informing Leonato that one of the servants has overheard part of Don Pedro and Claudio's conversation about speaking to Hero (scene ii):

    The prince and Count Claudio, walking in a thick-pleached
    alley in my orchard, were thus much overheard by a man of
    mine: the prince discovered to Claudio that he loved my niece
    your daughter and meant to acknowledge it this night in a
    dance; and, if he found her accordant, he meant to take the
    present time by the top and instantly <u>break with</u> you of it.

NAME: _____   DATE: _____

Vocabulary Review Quiz
for
Much Ado About Nothing
Act I

Directions: For each of the italicized words in the sentences below, determine
which letter best reflects the use of the word in this context. Place
the letter corresponding to your answer in the space to the left of the
item number.

____1.   When Beatrice uses *subscribed for* she suggests that Benedick (her
uncle's fool)

   A. chased away Cupid.
   B. bribed Cupid.
   C. vouched for Cupid.
   D. denied Cupid.
   E. began to play Cupid.

____2.   When Leonato explains that there's "a merry war *betwixt*" Beatrice
and Benedick, he means that there is

   A. a battle between the two.
   B. romance in bloom.
   C. no hope for the relationship.
   D. peace between the two.
   E. a chance of warfare soon.

____3.   When Beatrice refers to a *squarer*, she means a

   A. building tool.
   B. nerd.
   C. quarreler or ruffian.
   D. quiet man.
   E. learned man.

____4.   When Benedick insults Beatrice by calling her a *continuer*, he means
that Beatrice is

   A. a horse.
   B. unpleasant to be around.
   C. the great love of his life.
   D. engaged to be married.
   E. in love with him.

© 1997 by The Center for Applied Research in Education

_____5.   When Beatrice applies *jade* to Benedick, she is showing that she

    A. likes Benedick.
    B. scorns him.
    C. wants him.
    D. praises him.
    E. esteems him.

_____6.   When Claudio accuses Don Pedro of trying *"to fetch me in,"* he means that he's

    A. hopeful.
    B. skeptical.
    C. wary.
    D. in love.
    E. afraid.

_____7.   When Don Pedro tells Benedick to *"temporize* with the hours," he means that Benedick will

    A. eventually marry.
    B. never marry.
    C. marry Beatrice.
    D. remain a bachelor.
    E. see the error of his ways.

_____8.   As Don Pedro uses *once*, he means

    A. one time only.
    B. many times.
    C. eventually.
    D. once for all.
    E. never.

_____9.   When Antonio uses *event*, he means

    A. marriage.
    B. situation.
    C. account.
    D. outcome.
    E. divorce.

_____10.   As Antonio uses *break*, he means

    A. destroy.
    B. separate.
    C. slow.
    D. inform.
    E. discredit.

ACT II

NAME: _____   DATE: _____

Focusing Activities
for
Much Ado About Nothing
Scenarios for Improvisation
Act II

Directions: Presented below are locations and situations involving characters. As your teacher directs you, but before reading an individual scene, pretend to be one of the characters and act out the situation. Don't worry about speaking like the characters in Shakespeare's plays, just try to imagine how you would react to the situation and use your own language. Your teacher may give you a few minutes to discuss what you would like to do with the other performers. Your teacher will probably ask you to act out your scene for others in the class. When you finish, your teacher may ask your classmates to discuss what they've seen.

scene i.   *Scene*: The ball at Leonato's house.

Characters: Claudio, Don John

Situation: Don Pedro has danced with Hero and won her for Claudio. Both Claudio and Don John have seen Don Pedro ask Hero to marry him but haven't been close enough to hear what he said to her. What does Don John tell Claudio and how does he respond?

scene ii.   *Scene*: A hall in Leonato's house.

Characters: Don John, Borachio

Situation: Don John's first attempt to wreck Claudio and Hero's marriage has failed. Borachio comes up with a new plan to split up Claudio and Hero. What does he propose?

scene iii.   *Scene*: Leonato's orchard

Characters: Don Pedro, Claudio, Leonato, and Benedick

Situation: Don Pedro has enlisted the help of Claudio and Leonato to trick Benedick into believing that Beatrice is in love with him. Knowing that he can overhear what they say, improvise their conversation that would convince Benedick that Beatrice loves him.

63

Focusing Activities
for
Much Ado About Nothing
Small Group Discussion Questions
Act II

Directions: Before reading scenes in Act II, discuss the questions in small groups. You may want to make notes about your discussion so you can share them with classmates or refer back to them after you've read the scene.

scene i.

1. What possible problems do you anticipate for Don Pedro's plan to disguise himself as Claudio and ask Hero to marry him?

2. At the ball most guests will be wearing masks. In what ways might a masked Beatrice treat a masked Benedick differently and how might he respond?

scene ii.

1. When Don John learns that Leonato has consented for Claudio to marry Hero, how do you think he might react?

2. What plan might Don John come up with to spoil the wedding of Claudio and Hero?

scene iii.

1. Don Pedro has enlisted the help of Claudio and Leonato to trick Benedick into falling in love with Beatrice. What might they do to make Benedick believe that Beatrice is in love with him?

2. How do you think Benedick might act towards Beatrice once he's been convince that she is in love with him?

© 1997 by The Center for Applied Research in Education

NAME: _____ DATE: _____

Focusing Activities
for
Much Ado About Nothing
Speculation Journal
Act II

Directions: This activity is to help you become involved actively with reading the play by helping you to determine a definite purpose for reading. Before you read these scenes in Act II, take a few minutes to respond in writing to the questions below. Don't worry about correct answers here. Use your own experience, what you know, or what you may have heard about the play to speculate about what you think might happen. After reading a scene, you may find that characters reacted differently than you thought. Don't worry about these differences; just make note of them because you will have opportunities to share these differences in other activities.

scene i.

1. What do you think might go wrong with Don Pedro's plan to disguise himself as Claudio and ask Hero to marry him?

2. At the ball, how might Beatrice and Benedick act toward each other when each is wearing a mask?

3. Because we know Don John is a villain who has vowed revenge on Don Pedro, what do you think he might do to spoil Don Pedro and Claudio's plans for the masked ball?

scene ii.

1. We know that Don John is a villain who has vowed revenge on Don Pedro. How do you expect Don John to react to the news that Leonato has consented for Claudio to marry Hero?

65

2. If you were Don John, how would you plan to break up the wedding between Claudio and Hero?

scene iii. If you wanted to trick Benedick into believing that Beatrice was in love with him, what might you do?

After reading Act II: Now that you have finished reading Act II, which of your speculations were most like the action of the characters in the play? How do you account for them? Which ones were least like the action of the play? Why do you think you speculated as you did?

Prereading Activity
for
Much Ado About Nothing
Vocabulary
Act II

Directions: Shakespeare uses the following words in Act II. The section below provides a brief definition of each word and provides a sentence to illustrate its meaning. You may wish to review the words for a particular scene immediately before reading it.

Definitions.

scene i

1. **shrewd:**   (adj.) shrewish, mischievous, scolding.
   Example: Beatrice is known throughout Messina for her *shrewd* tongue.

2. **counterfeit:**   (v.) imitate, mimic.
   Example: While the teacher was out of the room, the class clown began to *counterfeit* her.

3. **honestly:**   (adj.) honorably.
   Example: Don Pedro woos Hero and *honestly* surrenders her to Claudio.

scene ii

4. **misuse:**   (v.) mislead; abuse with words.
   Example: Borachio's plan to break up Claudio's wedding involves *misusing* Hero's reputation.

scene iii

5. **daff:**   (v.) turn aside.
   Example: Despite the flowers, candy, and expensive presents, the young girl continued to *daff* the old man's efforts to marry her.

Prereading Activity
for
Much Ado About Nothing
Plot Summaries
Act II

Directions: To help you better understand and follow *Much Ado About Nothing*, read the summary of a specific scene before you begin to read it. If you get lost during the scene, you can refer to the summary.

Act II, scene i

A hall in Leonato's house, the evening immediately following. Enter Leonato, Antonio, Hero, Beatrice, Margaret, and Ursula. Leonato and Antonio note that Don John was not at supper. Beatrice comments that Don John looks tartly, giving her heartburn. Hero responds that he is melancholy by nature. Beatrice uses the opportunity to verbally attack Benedick by describing the perfect man as a midpoint between Don John who says nothing and Benedick who never stops talking.

Leonato chides Beatrice about getting a husband now that it looks as if Hero will soon be married. She makes light of the possibility of finding a suitable man.

Soon the masked ball begins. Don Pedro quickly selects Hero for a dance so he can press Claudio's case with her. Don Pedro pretends to be Claudio and declares his love for Hero. Borachio dances with Margaret, and Antonio with Ursula. Beatrice pretends not to recognize Benedick as her partner, so she paints a ridiculous portrait of Benedick.

Don John and Borachio recognize Claudio, although he is still masked. They pretend to mistake Claudio for Benedick. Don John, to begin getting his revenge, tells Claudio that the Prince is in love with Hero and is wooing her himself. Claudio believes this is the case and is saddened.

Benedick tries to cheer up his friend but fails, so Claudio leaves.

Benedick tells Don Pedro about Beatrice's insulting description of him, and that he couldn't bring himself to remove his mask and defend himself. Beatrice approaches and Benedick asks for some quest that will take him far away from her presence. Benedick leaves. Beatrice notes that when Claudio returns he is sad. Don Pedro informs Claudio that Leonato has given his consent for Claudio to marry Hero.

© 1997 by The Center for Applied Research in Education

Don Pedro and Beatrice jest about her getting a husband. When the Prince offers to find her one, Beatrice replies that she would prefer a brother of the Prince if he had one. When the Prince offers himself, she replies that he is "too costly to wear every day" and that she only speaks in jest. She then leaves.

Leonato and Don Pedro decide that Beatrice would make a good wife for Benedick. They enlist the aid of Claudio and Hero to bring the two together.

Act II, scene ii

The hall, immediately following. Don John is unhappy about the approaching marriage of Claudio to Hero. Borachio has a plan to convince Claudio and Don Pedro that Hero is unfaithful. Don John will go to Don Pedro and Claudio and say that in deference to Claudio's noble character and friendship with the Prince he has proof that Hero is not a suitable match for Claudio. Borachio will have Margaret, Hero's attendant, dress in Hero's clothes and stage a meeting with Borachio that Don Pedro and Claudio will witness. When they hear Borachio address Margaret as Hero while the attendant stands in the window of Hero's chamber, they will be convinced that Hero is unfaithful, so Claudio will refuse to marry her.

Act II, scene iii

In Leonato's orchard before dinner the next day. Benedick enters and ponders whether he could ever fall in love as Claudio has. He reflects that many of the women he's met have singular qualities that would attract him. One is fair; another is wise; another virtuous. The perfect woman would be all these things. Hearing Don Pedro and Claudio approaching, he hides so he can eavesdrop.

Don Pedro urges Balthazar to sing before beginning their conversation that Benedick will overhear. In the conversation they're staging for Benedick, Don Pedro, Claudio, and Leonato express their concern for Beatrice who is hopelessly in love with Benedick. They decry the irony that she must be so in love with a man she has ridiculed so publicly. If she were to tell Benedick how she truly felt, he would only take it as an opportunity to humiliate her in public for her description of him at the ball. They conclude that Beatrice will have to deal with her emotions as well as she can without telling Benedick how she truly feels. They decide to send Beatrice to call Benedick to dinner and then leave.

Benedick comes out of hiding and comments upon what he has heard. He is convinced that Beatrice is in love with him, and will return her love. When Beatrice comes to call Benedick to dinner, he thanks her but she responds as she always has and verbally spars with him. When she leaves, Benedick convinces himself that her actions prove that she loves him.

Class Period:

CHARACTER ASSIGNMENTS FOR ORAL READING GROUPS

Much Ado About Nothing

Session 2: Act II, scene i

Characters	_Group 1_	_Group 2_	_Group 3_	_Group 4_
Leonato	_____	_____	_____	_____
Antonio, Borachio	_____	_____	_____	_____
Beatrice	_____	_____	_____	_____
Hero	_____	_____	_____	_____
Margaret	_____	_____	_____	_____
Ursula	_____	_____	_____	_____
Claudio	_____	_____	_____	_____
Don Pedro	_____	_____	_____	_____

Class Period:

CHARACTER ASSIGNMENTS FOR ORAL READING GROUPS

Much Ado About Nothing

Session 3: Act II, scenes ii, iii

Characters	*Group 1*	*Group 2*	*Group 3*	*Group 4*
Borachio				
Don John				
Benedick				
Beatrice				
Don Pedro				
Claudio				
Leonato				
Boy, Balthazar				

During-Reading Activity
for
Much Ado About Nothing
Character Diary 2
Act II, scene i

Directions: Use the space below to record your character's reactions to the events of the first scene in Act II of *Much Ado About Nothing*. Remember to include a summary of events, explain how your character learned of them, and give your character's reactions to them. If you need additional room, use the back of this sheet.

The Personal Diary of

_____
(character's name)

The banquet hall of Leonato's house
The same evening

_____
_____
_____
_____
_____
_____
_____
_____
_____
_____
_____
_____
_____
_____

During-Reading Activity
for
Much Ado About Nothing
Character Diary 3
Act II, scenes ii, iii

Directions: Use the space below to record your character's reactions to the events of the final two scenes in Act II of *Much Ado About Nothing*. Remember to include a summary of events, explain how your character learned of them, and give your character's reactions to them. If you need additional room, use the back of this sheet.

The Personal Diary of

_____
(character's name)

The banquet hall of Leonato's house
Later the same evening, after the ball

_____

_____

_____

_____

_____

_____

Leonato's garden
Late afternoon a day or two later

_____

_____

_____

_____

_____

_____

During-Reading Activity
for
Much Ado About Nothing
Viewing Act II, scenes i and ii
Don Pedro Wins Hero; Don John and Borachio Plot

Directions: After you've read these scenes, viewing a film or video version may help you better understand how the text translates into the characters' actions. Although you may want to keep your copy of the play handy, don't be surprised if the actors' script varies from yours. Film scripts often delete or reorder the lines in the play. You may want to note questions you need to ask your teacher afterward. After viewing the scene, take a few minutes to respond to the questions below.

1. How do the nighttime setting and the wearing of masks during the ball enhance the action of the play?

2. How do Hero, Beatrice, Margaret, and Ursula react to their partners during the scene?

3. How does Claudio react to what he sees during the scene?

4. How do the actors' facial expressions, tones of voice, and gestures enhance Shakespeare's words?

NAME: _____ DATE: _____

During-Reading Activity
for
Much Ado About Nothing
Guide to Character Development: Hero
Act II

Shakespeare reveals his characters in four ways:

- through what the characters say to other characters in dialogue;
- through what the characters reveal about their thoughts through long speeches to the audience called *soliloquies*;
- through what other characters say about them;
- through what they do, their actions.

As you read the play, examine the following scenes for what they reveal about Hero's character and fill in the chart briefly using your own words. If you need more room, use the back of the page.

Scene	*What Hero says, does, or what others say about her*	*What this reveals about Hero's character*
Act II, scene i Hero agrees to walk with Don Pedro		
Act II, scene i Hero agrees to marry Claudio		

During-Reading Activity
for
Much Ado About Nothing
Guide to Character Development: Beatrice
Act II

Shakespeare reveals his characters in four ways:

- through what the characters say to other characters in dialogue;
- through what the characters reveal about their thoughts through long speeches to the audience called *soliloquies*;
- through what other characters say about them;
- through what they do, their actions.

As you read the play, examine the following scenes for what they reveal about Beatrice's character and fill in the chart briefly using your own words. If you need more room, use the back of the page.

Scene	What Beatrice says, does, or what others say about her	What this reveals about Beatrice's character
Act II, scene i Beatrice comments upon Don John's melancholy character		
Act II, scene i Beatrice disdains marrying any man with a beard		
Act II, scene i Beatrice describes Benedick negatively to her masked partner (Benedick)		
Act II, scene i Beatrice prompts Hero to kiss Claudio		
Act II, scene i Beatrice flirts with Don Pedro		

NAME: _____   DATE: _____

During-Reading Activity
for
Much Ado About Nothing

Guide to Character Development: Benedick
Act II

Shakespeare reveals his characters in four ways:

- ☙ through what the characters say to other characters in dialogue;
- ☙ through what the characters reveal about their thoughts through long speeches to the audience called *soliloquies*;
- ☙ through what other characters say about them;
- ☙ through what they do, their actions.

As you read the play, examine the following scenes for what they reveal about Benedick's character and fill in the chart briefly using your own words. If you need more room, use the back of the page.

Scene	What Benedick says, does, or what others say about him	What this reveals about Benedick's character
Act II, scene i Benedick remains silent while Beatrice describes him negatively		
Act II, scene i Benedick tries to cheer up Claudio when Claudio believes Don Pedro has won Hero for himself		
Act II, scene i Benedick describes to Don Pedro how Beatrice misused him		

Scene	What Benedick says, does, or what others say about him	What this reveals about Benedick's character
Act II, scene i Benedick desires a quest from Don Pedro so he doesn't have to be in Beatrice's company		
Act II, scene iii Benedick describes his ideal woman		
Act II, scene iii Benedick overhears Don Pedro, Claudio, and Leonato describe how hopelessly in love Beatrice is with him		
Act II, scene iii Benedick, after thanking Beatrice for calling him to supper, convinces himself that Beatrice's attitude toward him has changed		

NAME: _____   DATE: _____

During-Reading Activity
for
Much Ado About Nothing
Guide to Character Development: Claudio
Act II

Shakespeare reveals his characters in four ways:

- through what the characters say to other characters in dialogue;
- through what the characters reveal about their thoughts through long speeches to the audience called *soliloquies*;
- through what other characters say about them;
- through what they do, their actions.

As you read the play, examine the following scenes for what they reveal about Claudio's character and fill in the chart briefly using your own words. If you need more room, use the back of the page.

Scene	*What Claudio says, does, or what others say about him*	*What this reveals about Claudio's character*
Act II, scene i Claudio allows Don Pedro to win Hero for him		
Act II, scene i Claudio is easily convinced by Don John that Don Pedro means to have Hero for himself		
Act II, scene i Leonato agrees to the marriage of Hero and Claudio		
Act II, scene iii Claudio helps Don Pedro and Leonato trick Benedick into thinking that Beatrice loves him		

During-Reading Activity
for
Much Ado About Nothing
Guide to Character Development: Don Pedro
Act II

Shakespeare reveals his characters in four ways:

- through what the characters say to other characters in dialogue;
- through what the characters reveal about their thoughts through long speeches to the audience called *soliloquies*;
- through what other characters say about them;
- through what they do, their actions.

As you read the play, examine the following scenes for what they reveal about Don Pedro's character and fill in the chart briefly using your own words. If you need more room, use the back of the page.

Scene	What Don Pedro says, does, or what others say about him	What this reveals about Don Pedro's character
Act II, scene i Don Pedro wins Hero for Claudio		
Act II, scene i Don Pedro listens to Benedick's complaints about Beatrice		
Act II, scene i Don Pedro gives Hero to Claudio		

Scene	What Don Pedro says, does, or what others say about him	What this reveals about Don Pedro's character
Act II, scene i Don Pedro decides that Benedick and Beatrice should be tricked into loving each other		
Act II, scene ii Don Pedro, with the help of Claudio and Leonato, tricks Benedick into thinking that Beatrice loves him		

During-Reading Activity
for
Much Ado About Nothing
Guide to Character Development: Leonato
Act II

Shakespeare reveals his characters in four ways:

- ♨ through what the characters say to other characters in dialogue;
- ♨ through what the characters reveal about their thoughts through long speeches to the audience called *soliloquies*;
- ♨ through what other characters say about them;
- ♨ through what they do, their actions.

As you read the play, examine the following scenes for what they reveal about Leonato's character and fill in the chart briefly using your own words. If you need more room, use the back of the page.

Scene	What Leonato says, does, or what others say about him	What this reveals about Leonato's character
Act II, scene ii Leonato reprimands Beatrice for her shrewd tongue		
Act II, scene ii Leonato consents to the marriage of Hero and Claudio		
Act II, scene ii Leonato helps Don Pedro and Claudio trick Benedick into thinking that Beatrice loves him		

NAME: _____   DATE: _____

During-Reading Activity
for
Much Ado About Nothing
Guide to Character Development: Don John
Act II

Shakespeare reveals his characters in four ways:

- through what the characters say to other characters in dialogue;
- through what the characters reveal about their thoughts through long speeches to the audience called *soliloquies*;
- through what other characters say about them;
- through what they do, their actions.

As you read the play, examine the following scenes for what they reveal about Don John's character and fill in the chart briefly using your own words. If you need more room, use the back of the page.

Scene	What Don John says, does, or what others say about him	What this reveals about Don John's character
Act II, scene i Don John tells Claudio that Don Pedro woos Hero for himself		
Act II, scene ii Don John and Borachio plan to discredit Hero		

During-Reading Activity
for
Much Ado About Nothing
Guide to Character Development: Borachio
Act II

Shakespeare reveals his characters in four ways:

- ❧ through what the characters say to other characters in dialogue;
- ❧ through what the characters reveal about their thoughts through long speeches to the audience called *soliloquies*;
- ❧ through what other characters say about them;
- ❧ through what they do, their actions.

As you read the play, examine the following scenes for what they reveal about Borachio's character and fill in the chart briefly using your own words. If you need more room, use the back of the page.

Scene	What Borachio says, does, or what others say about him	What this reveals about Borachio's character
Act II, scene i Don John and Borachio tell Claudio that Don Pedro woos Hero for himself		
Act II, scene ii Don John and Borachio plan to discredit Hero		

During-Reading Activity
for
Much Ado About Nothing
Guide to Character Development: Margaret
Act II

Shakespeare reveals his characters in four ways:

- ❧ through what the characters say to other characters in dialogue;
- ❧ through what the characters reveal about their thoughts through long speeches to the audience called *soliloquies*;
- ❧ through what other characters say about them;
- ❧ through what they do, their actions.

As you read the play, examine the following scene for what it reveals about Margaret's character and fill in the chart briefly using your own words. If you need more room, use the back of the page.

Scene	What Margaret says, does, or what others say about her	What this reveals about Margaret's character
Act II, scene i Margaret pairs up with Borachio		

85

Postreading Activity
for
Much Ado About Nothing
Comprehension Check
Act II

Directions: After you've read all of Act II, use the following questions to check how well you've understood what you've read. For each question, select the most appropriate answer from the choices listed below it. Place the letter corresponding to your answer in the space to the left of the item number.

_____1.   According to Beatrice and Leonato (scene i) the ideal man would have

   A. half of Benedick's tongue.
   B. half of Don John's melancholy.
   C. a good leg and a good foot.
   D. enough money in his purse.
   E. all these characteristics.

_____2.   During the masked ball, why is Beatrice able to further deride Benedick while dancing with him?

   A. She wishes to get even for his cutting her off earlier in the day.
   B. He doesn't wish to reveal his true identity.
   C. She doesn't know to whom she is talking.
   D. He doesn't recognize with whom he's dancing.
   E. He, like Don Pedro, plans to ask his partner to marry him.

_____3.   During the ball, Don John manages to convince Claudio that

   A. Don Pedro has no interest in Hero.
   B. Don Pedro has won Hero for Claudio.
   C. Don Pedro has won Hero for Benedick.
   D. Don Pedro has won Hero for himself.
   E. Don Pedro has won Hero for Don John.

_____4.   After the ball, Borachio reveals his plan to disrupt the wedding between Claudio and Hero by

   A. discrediting Claudio's reputation.
   B. discrediting Don Pedro's reputation.
   C. discrediting Beatrice's reputation.
   D. discrediting Hero's reputation.
   E. discrediting Margaret's reputation.

____5.   Don Pedro, Leonato, and Claudio trick Benedick into believing that Beatrice is in love with him by

A. allowing him to eavesdrop on their conversation.
B. sending him a phony letter.
C. having Hero pretend to be Beatrice and telling him so.
D. having Margaret pretend to be Beatrice and telling him so.
E. allowing him to overhear a conversation between Hero and Margaret.

Postreading Activity
for
Much Ado About Nothing
Small Group Discussion to Check Comprehension
Act II

Directions: After you've read all of Act II, discuss each of the following questions in small groups briefly. Use the space below each question to note points you may wish to share later. If you need more room, use the back of the page.

1.   According to Beatrice and Leonato in scene i, what would be the characteristics of the perfect man for Beatrice?

2.   How would you characterize the interactions between each of the following couples during the masked ball: Don Pedro and Hero; Ursula and Antonio; Margaret and Borachio?

3.   What do Don John and Borachio plan to do to break up the marriage of Claudio and Hero?

4.   Why do you think Benedick is so easily convinced that Beatrice is in love with him after overhearing the staged conversation among Don Pedro, Leonato, and Claudio?

5.   In what ways does Benedick misinterpret Beatrice's words and actions at the end of Act II, scene iii?

Postreading Activity
for
Much Ado About Nothing
Critical Thinking Questions
Act II

Directions: To help you develop your understanding of Act II, as your teacher directs you, take time to think about and discuss these questions. The first question is the focus question and is the point of the discussion. Don't be concerned that you may not be able to answer this question at first. Proceed to the exploration questions and then return to the focus question.

Focus Question. If you were either Claudio or Benedick, what would make you less willing to accept the comments of others about your personal relationships?

Exploration Questions.

1. What are the stereotypical characteristics of the hero, heroine, and villain in popular culture?

2. What sorts of issues tend to make teenage couples jealous?

3. How does the relationship between Beatrice and Benedick differ from the one between Claudio and Hero?

4. Which characters in *Much Ado About Nothing* seem to reflect the stereotypical images of the hero, heroine, or villain?

5. In what ways are Claudio's insecurities about Hero comparable to how teenagers act today?

Postreading Activity
for
Much Ado About Nothing

Language Exploration
Figurative Language: Personification
Act II

We have seen how Shakespeare uses simile and metaphor to develop figurative language. Like Shakespeare, we also use other devices to express abstract ideas more concretely, among them *personification*. We use personification to give human characteristics to inanimate or nonhuman things. We may say that "Love is blind," or argue with the soft drink machine that "eats" our change.

In Act I, scene i, Benedick refers to Beatrice as Lady Disdain. She then makes the following retort that personifies both disdain and courtesy:

&

Is it possible <u>disdain should die while she hath such</u>
<u>meet food to feed it</u> as Signior Benedick? <u>Courtesy itself</u>
<u>must convert to disdain</u> if you come <u>in her presence</u>.

&

Directions: The following passages contain examples of personification. Working in pairs, small groups, or as your teacher directs, review each passage within the context of the play and develop an interpretation of the passage. You may wish to review the quotations within the fuller context of the particular speech.

1.   Benedick continuing his verbal battle with Beatrice (Act I, scene i):

&

Then is courtesy a turn-coat.

&

2. Beatrice advising Hero on wooing, wedding, and repenting (Act II, scene i):

    ❧

    For, hear me, Hero: wooing, wedding, and repenting, is as a
    Scotch jig, a measure, and a cinque pace: the first suit is hot
    hasty, like a Scotch jig, and full as fantastical; the wedding,
    mannerly-modest, as a measure, full of state and ancientry;
    and <u>then comes repentance and, with his bad legs</u>, falls into
    the cinque pace faster and faster, till he sink into his grave.

    ❧

3. Ursula jesting with Antonio at the masked ball (Act II, scene i):

    ❧

    Come, come, do you think I do not know you by your
    excellent wit? Can virtue hide itself?

    ❧

4. Claudio beginning to respond to Don John's news that Don Pedro courts Hero for himself (Act II, scene i):

    ❧

    Friendship is constant in all other things
    Save in the office and affairs of love:

    ❧

5. Claudio continuing with his response to Don John (Act II, scene i):

    ❧

    Therefore, all hearts in love use their own tongues;

    ❧

6. Claudio continuing further with his response to Don John (Act II, scene i):

    ❧

    Let every eye negotiate for itself
    And trust no agent;

    ❧

91

7. Claudio concluding his response to Don John (Act II, scene i):

    ❧

    for beauty is a witch
    Against whose charms faith melteth into blood.

    ❧

8. Benedick complaining to Don Pedro about how Beatrice abused him during the ball (Act II, scene i):

    ❧

    O, she misused me past the endurance of a block! an oak
    but with one green leaf on it would have answered her;

    ❧

9. Benedick concluding his complaint about how Beatrice abused him (Act II, scene i):

    ❧

    my very visor began to assume life and scold with her.

    ❧

10. Claudio's response to learn that Hero and he are to be married (Act II, scene i):

    ❧

    Silence is the perfectest herald of joy.

    ❧

Postreading Activity
for
Much Ado About Nothing
Vocabulary in Context
Act II

Directions: In each of the passages below you will find one of the words from the prereading vocabulary list for Act II. Review the definitions given in the prereading vocabulary. Working individually, in pairs, or in small groups as your teacher directs, examine each of the underlined words in the following passages from Act II. For each word, use the appropriate meaning and develop a brief interpretation of the passage within the context of the play.

scene i.

1.   Leonato commenting to Beatrice about her sharp tongue:

> &

> By my troth, niece, thou wilt never get thee a husband,
> if thou be so <u>shrewd</u> of thy tongue.

> &

2.   Ursula recognizes Antonio during the masked ball; he denies it:

> &

> To tell you true, I <u>counterfeit</u> him.

> &

3.   When Benedick tells Don Pedro that Claudio believes that he has wooed Hero for himself, the Prince promises to set Claudio straight. Benedick then replies:

> &

> If their singing answer your saying, by my faith,
> you say <u>honestly</u>.

> &

scene ii.

4. Borachio bragging to Don John that he has a plan to disrupt the pending marriage of Claudio and Hero:

    ❧

    *Proof enough to <u>misuse</u> the prince, to vex Claudio, to undo
    Hero and kill Leonato. Look you for any other issue?*

    ❧

scene iii.

5. Don Pedro speaking to Leonato, trying to convince Benedick, who is eavesdropping, that Beatrice is in love with him:

    ❧

    *I would have <u>daffed</u> all other respects and made her half
    myself.*

    ❧

Vocabulary Review Quiz
for
Much Ado About Nothing
Act II

Directions: For each of the italicized words in the sentences below, determine which letter best reflects the use of the word in this context. Place the letter corresponding to your answer in the space to the left of the item number.

____1. When Leonato accuses Beatrice of having a *shrewd* tongue, he means

   A. troublesome.
   B. overbearing.
   C. scolding.
   D. jealous.
   E. mean.

____2. When Antonio says that he *counterfeits* Antonio, he means

   A. imitates or mimics.
   B. falsifies.
   C. forges.
   D. embezzles.
   E. impersonates.

____3. Because Benedick views Don Pedro as one who speaks *honestly*, he means

   A. honestly.
   B. honorably.
   C. courteously.
   D. nobly.
   E. effortlessly.

____4. When Borachio mentions *misuse*, he means

   A. turn aside.
   B. squander.
   C. abuse with words.
   D. beat up.
   E. cheat upon.

_____ 5.   When Don Pedro uses *daffed*, he means

     A. crazed.
     B. immobile.
     C. turned aside.
     D. turned around.
     E. turned about.

ACT III

© 1997 by The Center for Applied Research in Education

NAME: _____   DATE: _____

Focusing Activities
for
Much Ado About Nothing
Scenarios for Improvisation
Act III

Directions: Presented below are locations and situations involving characters. As your teacher directs you, but before reading an individual scene, pretend to be one of the characters and act out the situation. Don't worry about speaking like the characters in Shakespeare's plays, just try to imagine how you would react to the situation and use your own language. Your teacher may give you a few minutes to discuss what you would like to do with the other performers. Your teacher will probably ask you to act out your scene for others in the class. When you finish, your teacher may ask your classmates to discuss what they've seen.

scene i.   *Scene*: Leonato's garden.

Characters: Hero, Ursula, Beatrice.

Situation: Hero has enlisted the help of Ursula and Margaret to trick Beatrice into believing that Benedick is in love with her. Knowing that she can overhear what they say, improvise a conversation that would convince Beatrice that Benedick loves her.

scene ii.   *Scene*: A room in Leonato's house.

Characters: Don Pedro, Don John, Claudio.

Situation: Don John wishes to wreck the coming marriage of Claudio and Hero, which is planned for the next day. How does he convince his half brother and Claudio to come witness Margaret dressed as Hero being unfaithful and still maintain his credibility?

scene iii.   *Scene*: A street.

Characters: Borachio and Conrade.

Situation: Borachio has just come from using Margaret to carry out the plan to discredit Hero. Don John has just paid him a thousand ducats for the success of the plan. What does he say when he encounters his friend Conrade?

scene iv.   <u>*Scene*</u>: Hero's room.

<u>*Characters*</u>: Hero, Margaret, Beatrice.

<u>*Situation*</u>: As Hero prepares for her wedding, she and Margaret notice that Beatrice is strangely quiet. Suspecting she is in love with Benedick, they tease her about him. What do they say and what does she say in response?

NAME: _____   DATE: _____

Focusing Activities
for
Much Ado About Nothing
Small Group Discussion Questions
Act III

Directions: Before reading scenes in Act III, discuss the questions in small groups. You may want to make notes about your discussion so you can share them with classmates or refer back to them after you've read the scene.

scene i.

1.   If you were Hero, what "evidence" would you have to present to Beatrice to convince her that Benedick was in love with her?

2.   If you were Beatrice, how do you think you would respond to hearing such news?

scene ii.   If you were Don John, how would you go about convincing Don Pedro and Claudio to come with you to see "Hero" being unfaithful?

scene iii.   If you were Borachio and had been paid handsomely by Don John for making Hero seem unfaithful, what would you do once Don Pedro and Claudio had seen you with "Hero?"

scene iv.   If you were Hero preparing for your wedding and Beatrice came in strangely silent, what would you suspect was the cause of her silence and how might you treat her?

scene v.   If you were Leonato preparing for your only child's wedding, how patient do you think you would be with someone like Dogberry?

Focusing Activities
for
Much Ado About Nothing
Speculation Journal
Act III

Directions: This activity will help you become involved actively with reading the play by helping you to determine a definite purpose for reading. Before you read these scenes in Act III, take a few minutes to respond in writing to questions below. Don't worry about correct answers here. Use your own experience or what you have read in the play to speculate about what you think will happen. After reading a scene you may find that the characters reacted differently than you thought. Don't worry about these differences; just make note of them because you will have opportunities to share these differences in other activities.

scene i.

1.   How do you think Hero and the other women will go about convincing Beatrice that Benedick is in love with her?

2.   How do you think Beatrice will respond to hearing that Benedick is in love with her?

scene ii.   How do you think Don John will be able to prove to Don Pedro and Claudio that Hero is unfaithful?

scene iii.   Because Borachio will be paid well by Don John to make Hero appear unworthy of Claudio, what do you think Borachio will do once he has presented the proof to Don Pedro and Claudio?

© 1997 by The Center for Applied Research in Education

scene iv.   What might Hero and the other women conclude about a strange silence on the part of Beatrice on the eve of Hero's wedding?

scene v.   While Leonato prepares for Hero's wedding, how patient do you think he would be with someone as slow as Dogberry?

After reading Act III: Now that you have finished reading Act III, which of your speculations were most like the action of the characters in the play? How do you account for them? Which ones were least like the action of the play? Why do you think you speculated as you did?

Prereading Activity
for
Much Ado About Nothing
Vocabulary
Act III

Directions: Shakespeare uses the following words in Act III. The section below provides a brief definition of each word and provides a sentence to illustrate its meaning. You may wish to review the words for a particular scene immediately before reading it.

Definitions.

scene i

1. **pleached:**   (adv.) deliberately interwoven vines or branches in a formal garden used to form an arbor; braided.

    Example: The gardeners had skillfully *pleached* the branches of the trees so they formed a completely covered pathway through the garden.

scene ii

2. **warrant:**   (n.) assurance, justification.

    Example: Without sufficient *warrant*, the judge refused to have the suspect arrested.

scene iii

3. **reechy:**   (adj.) smoky, vaporous, steamy; obscured by smoke or vapor.

    Example: Because the Maasi tribes in southeastern Africa live in huts with little ventilation, anyone who enters their homes comes out with the *reechy* odor of smoke on their clothes.

4. **smirched**:   (adj.) stained, dirty, smudged.

    Example: After cleaning the fireplace, my face was *smirched* with soot.

scene iv

5. **apprehension**   (n.) understanding.

    Example: With a little practice, even our *apprehension* of Shakespeare's language improved.

Prereading Activity
for
Much Ado About Nothing
Plot Summaries
Act III

Directions: To help you better understand and follow *Much Ado About Nothing*, read the summary of a specific scene before you begin to read it. If you get lost during the scene, you can refer to the summary.

Act III, scene i

Leonato's orchard. Now that Claudio and Don Pedro have convinced Benedick that Beatrice is in love with him, Hero uses her attendants, Margaret and Ursula, to convince Beatrice that Benedick is hopelessly in love with her. Hero sends Margaret to Beatrice to tell her that Hero and Ursula are talking about her, while they walk in the garden. Knowing that Beatrice will come, Hero instructs Ursula to praise Benedick while Hero explains how hopelessly in love Benedick is with Beatrice.

Beatrice enters and hides behind the arbor where she believes she can eavesdrop more easily. Hero informs Ursula that Don Pedro has told her that Benedick is hopelessly in love with Beatrice. Benedick, however, cannot tell Beatrice because she is too proud, disdainful, and scornful of him. Hero further characterizes Beatrice as a woman who always criticizes any man as the opposite of what he is: if he were fair, she'd call him black; if he were tall, she'd call him lance-headed; if low, a badly cut agate; if well spoken, she would call him windy enough to turn a weather vane. Instead, Hero suggests she will go to Benedick and urge him to fight against his passionate love for Beatrice. Then Hero asks Ursula to go with her to select her clothes for the wedding the next day.

Once Beatrice is alone, she realizes much of how her cousin characterized her is true. She vows that if Benedick is so much in love with her, she will return his love.

Act III, scene ii

A room in Leonato's house. Don Pedro, Leonato, Claudio, and Benedick have been discussing the imminent wedding. Don Pedro tells Claudio that he will be leaving once Claudio and Hero are married. Claudio offers to accompany the Prince, but Don Pedro declines, saying that Benedick's company will be sufficient. Benedick enters and his friends notice that he is changed. He claims to have a toothache but his friends kid him about being in love. Benedick requests a word with Leonato and the two leave.

Don John enters and asks for a word with Don Pedro and Claudio. He springs his plot to discredit Hero's fidelity. He suggests that Hero is unfaithful. Both Don Pedro and Claudio are skeptical but agree to go with Don John that night at midnight to watch as Margaret, wearing Hero's clothes, is wooed by Borachio from below Hero's window.

Act III, scene iii   Dogberry, the Prince's constable, and Verges, his old assistant, enter with the other members of the watch. Dogberry gives the watchmen their instructions. Although the watchmen are inept, they soon encounter Borachio and Conrade. Borachio brags how Don John has given him a thousand ducats for his part in the plot to discredit Hero. Although the watchmen don't understand all of Borachio and Conrade's conversation, they recognize their villainy and arrest the two.

Act III, scene iv   Hero's rooms in Leonato's house. Hero, Ursula, and Margaret discuss the wedding attire. They tease Beatrice about being in love with Benedick. Beatrice is so changed that she can't reply as she normally would.

Act III, scene v   The hall in Leonato's house. Dogberry and Verges attempt to inform Leonato about the arrest of Borachio and Conrade. However, it takes Dogberry and Verges so long to get to the point that Leonato asks them to examine the men and then report to him later.

Class Period:

CHARACTER ASSIGNMENTS FOR ORAL READING GROUPS

Much Ado About Nothing

Session 4: Act III, scenes i, ii

Characters	_Group 1_	_Group 2_	_Group 3_	_Group 4_
Hero	___	___	___	___
Margaret, Don John	___	___	___	___
Ursula	___	___	___	___
Beatrice	___	___	___	___
Don Pedro	___	___	___	___
Claudio	___	___	___	___
Benedick	___	___	___	___
Leonato	___	___	___	___

Class Period:

CHARACTER ASSIGNMENTS FOR ORAL READING GROUPS
Much Ado About Nothing

Session 5: Act III, scenes iii, iv, v

Characters	*Group 1*	*Group 2*	*Group 3*	*Group 4*
Dogberry	——	——	——	——
Verges	——	——	——	——
First Watchman	——	——	——	——
Second Watchman	——	——	——	——
Borachio, Ursula	——	——	——	——
Conrade, Margaret	——	——	——	——
Hero, Leonato	——	——	——	——
Beatrice	——	——	——	——

During-Reading Activity
for
Much Ado About Nothing
Character Diary 4
Act III, scenes i, ii

Directions: Use the space below to record your character's reactions to the events of the first two scenes in Act III of *Much Ado About Nothing*. Remember to include a summary of events, explain how your character learned of them, and give your character's reactions to them. Because this act has five scenes, you may wish to record your character's entries as you read each scene. If you need additional room, use the back of this sheet.

The Personal Diary of

_____
(character's name)

Leonato's Garden
The afternoon before Hero and Claudio's wedding

_____
_____
_____
_____
_____
_____
_____
_____
_____
_____
_____
_____
_____
_____
_____

During-Reading Activity
for
Much Ado About Nothing
Character Diary 5
Act III, scenes iii, iv, v

Directions: Use the space below to record your character's reactions to the events of the last three scenes in Act III of *Much Ado About Nothing*. Remember to include a summary of events, explain how your character learned of them, and give your character's reactions to them. Because this act has five scenes, you may wish to record your character's entries as you read each scene. If you need additional room, use the back of this sheet.

The Personal Diary of

_____
(character's name)

A street in Messina
The evening before Claudio and Hero's wedding

_____
_____
_____
_____

Hero's room
The morning of Hero and Claudio's wedding

_____
_____
_____
_____

The hall in Leonato's house
The morning of the wedding

_____
_____
_____
_____

During-Reading Activity
for
Much Ado About Nothing
Viewing Act III, scene i
The Women Convince Beatrice That Benedick Is in Love with Her

Directions: After you've read this scene, viewing a film or video version may help you better understand how the text translates into the characters' actions. Although you may want to keep your copy of the play handy, don't be surprised if the actors' script varies from yours. Film scripts often delete or reorder the lines in the play. You may want to note questions you need to ask your teacher afterward. After viewing the scene, take a few minutes to respond to the questions below.

1.   How do the women's voices and gestures change once they know that Beatrice is eavesdropping?

2.   How does Beatrice respond to what she's hearing about Benedick?

3.   How do Hero and the others know that their trick has worked?

4.   How do the actors' facial expressions, tones of voice, and gestures enhance Shakespeare's words?

During-Reading Activity
for
Much Ado About Nothing
Guide to Character Development: Hero
Act III

Shakespeare reveals his characters in four ways:

- through what the characters say to other characters in dialogue;
- through what the characters reveal about their thoughts through long speeches to the audience called *soliloquies*;
- through what other characters say about them;
- through what they do, their actions.

As you read the play, examine the following scenes for what they reveal about Hero's character and fill in the chart briefly using your own words. If you need more room, use the back of the page.

Scene	What Hero says, does, or what others say about her	What this reveals about Hero's character
Act III, scene i Hero, Margaret, and Ursula convince Beatrice that Benedick is hopelessly in love with her		
Act III, scene iv Hero and Margaret tease Beatrice about being in love with Benedick		

During-Reading Activity
for
Much Ado About Nothing
Guide to Character Development: Beatrice
Act III

Shakespeare reveals his characters in four ways:

- through what the characters say to other characters in dialogue;
- through what the characters reveal about their thoughts through long speeches to the audience called *soliloquies*;
- through what other characters say about them;
- through what they do, their actions.

As you read the play, examine the following scenes for what they reveal about Beatrice's character and fill in the chart briefly using your own words. If you need more room, use the back of the page.

© 1997 by The Center for Applied Research in Education

Scene	*What Beatrice says, does, or what others say about her*	*What this reveals about Beatrice's character*
Act III, scene i Hero, Margaret, and Ursula convince Beatrice that Benedick is hopelessly in love with her		
Act III, scene i Beatrice recognizes the truth in her cousin's description of her		
Act III, scene i Beatrice fails to have snappy comebacks in response to the teasing of Hero and Margaret		

During-Reading Activity
for
Much Ado About Nothing
Guide to Character Development: Benedick
Act III

Shakespeare reveals his characters in four ways:

- through what the characters say to other characters in dialogue;
- through what the characters reveal about their thoughts through long speeches to the audience called *soliloquies*;
- through what other characters say about them;
- through what they do, their actions.

As you read the play, examine the following scenes for what they reveal about Benedick's character and fill in the chart briefly using your own words. If you need more room, use the back of the page.

Scene	*What Benedick says, does, or what others say about him*	*What this reveals about Benedick's character*
Act III, scene ii Benedick complains that he has a toothache when Don Pedro, Claudio, and Leonato kid him about being in love with Beatrice		

© 1997 by The Center for Applied Research in Education

NAME: _____   DATE: _____

During-Reading Activity
for
Much Ado About Nothing
Guide to Character Development: Claudio
Act III

Shakespeare reveals his characters in four ways:

- ❧ through what the characters say to other characters in dialogue;
- ❧ through what the characters reveal about their thoughts through long speeches to the audience called *soliloquies*;
- ❧ through what other characters say about them;
- ❧ through what they do, their actions.

As you read the play, examine the following scenes for what they reveal about Claudio's character and fill in the chart briefly using your own words. If you need more room, use the back of the page.

Scene	What Claudio says, does, or what others say about him	What this reveals about Claudio's character
Act III, scene ii Claudio, Don Pedro, and Leonato kid Benedick about being in love with Beatrice		
Act III, scene ii Don John encourages Claudio and Don Pedro to see for themselves that Hero is unchaste		

During-Reading Activity
for
Much Ado About Nothing
Guide to Character Development: Don Pedro
Act III

Shakespeare reveals his characters in four ways:

- through what the characters say to other characters in dialogue;
- through what the characters reveal about their thoughts through long speeches to the audience called *soliloquies*;
- through what other characters say about them;
- through what they do, their actions.

As you read the play, examine the following scenes for what they reveal about Don Pedro's character and fill in the chart briefly using your own words. If you need more room, use the back of the page.

Scene	*What Don Pedro says, does, or what others say about him*	*What this reveals about Don Pedro's character*
Act III, scene ii Claudio, Don Pedro, and Leonato kid Benedick about being in love with Beatrice		
Act III, scene ii Don John encourages Claudio and Don Pedro to see for themselves that Hero is unchaste		

© 1997 by The Center for Applied Research in Education

NAME: _____   DATE: _____

During-Reading Activity
for
Much Ado About Nothing
Guide to Character Development: Leonato
Act III

Shakespeare reveals his characters in four ways:

- through what the characters say to other characters in dialogue;
- through what the characters reveal about their thoughts through long speeches to the audience called *soliloquies*;
- through what other characters say about them;
- through what they do, their actions.

As you read the play, examine the following scene for what it reveals about Leonato's character and fill in the chart briefly using your own words. If you need more room, use the back of the page.

Scene	What Leonato says, does, or what others say about him	What this reveals about Leonato's character
Act III, scene ii Claudio, Don Pedro, and Leonato kid Benedick about being in love with Beatrice		

NAME: _____   DATE: _____

During-Reading Activity
for
Much Ado About Nothing
Guide to Character Development: Don John
Act III

Shakespeare reveals his characters in four ways:

❧ through what the characters say to other characters in dialogue;

❧ through what the characters reveal about their thoughts through long speeches to the audience called *soliloquies*;

❧ through what other characters say about them;

❧ through what they do, their actions.

As you read the play, examine the following scenes for what they reveal about Don John's character and fill in the chart briefly using your own words. If you need more room, use the back of the page.

Scene	What Don John says, does, or what others say about him	What this reveals about Don John's character
Act III, scene ii Don John convinces Don Pedro and Claudio to witness Hero being unfaithful		
Act III, scene iii Don John pays Borachio a thousand ducats for helping discredit Hero's reputation		

NAME: _____   DATE: _____

During-Reading Activity
for
Much Ado About Nothing
Guide to Character Development: Borachio
Act III

Shakespeare reveals his characters in four ways:

- through what the characters say to other characters in dialogue;
- through what the characters reveal about their thoughts through long speeches to the audience called *soliloquies*;
- through what other characters say about them;
- through what they do, their actions.

As you read the play, examine the following scene for what it reveals about Borachio's character and fill in the chart briefly using your own words. If you need more room, use the back of the page.

Scene	*What Borachio says, does, or what others say about him*	*What this reveals about Borachio's character*
Act III, scene iii Borachio brags about helping discredit Hero and receiving a thousand ducats for his part		

119

During-Reading Activity
for
Much Ado About Nothing
Guide to Character Development: Margaret
Act III

Shakespeare reveals his characters in four ways:

- through what the characters say to other characters in dialogue;
- through what the characters reveal about their thoughts through long speeches to the audience called *soliloquies*;
- through what other characters say about them;
- through what they do, their actions.

As you read the play, examine the following scenes for what they reveal about Margaret's character and fill in the chart briefly using your own words. If you need more room, use the back of the page.

Scene	*What Margaret says, does, or what others say about her*	*What this reveals about Margaret's character*
Act III, scene i Hero, Margaret, and Ursula convince Beatrice that Benedick is hopelessly in love with her		
Act III, scene ii Margaret wears Hero's clothes and goes to the window to call to Borachio		

NAME: _____   DATE: _____

During-Reading Activity
for
Much Ado About Nothing
Guide to Character Development: Dogberry
Act III

Shakespeare reveals his characters in four ways:

- through what the characters say to other characters in dialogue;
- through what the characters reveal about their thoughts through long speeches to the audience called *soliloquies*;
- through what other characters say about them;
- through what they do, their actions.

As you read the play, examine the following scenes for what they reveal about Dogberry's character and fill in the chart briefly using your own words. If you need more room, use the back of the page.

Scene	What Dogberry says, does, or what others say about him	What this reveals about Dogberry's character
Act III, scene iii Dogberry gives his charge to the watch		
Act III, scene v Dogberry can't get to the point in telling Leonato that the watch has arrested Borachio and Conrade		

121

Postreading Activity
for
Much Ado About Nothing
Comprehension Check
Act III

Directions: After you've read all of Act III, use the following questions to check how well you've understood what you've read. For each question, select the most appropriate answer from the choices listed below it. Place the letter corresponding to your answer in the space to the left of the item number.

____1.   How does Hero get Beatrice to eavesdrop on their conversation?

A. She sends Ursula to tell Beatrice that Hero is talking about her.
B. She sends Margaret to tell Beatrice that Hero is talking about her.
C. She sends Benedick to tell Beatrice that Hero is talking about her.
D. She sends Don Pedro to tell Beatrice that Hero is talking about her.
E. She sends Claudio to tell Beatrice that Hero is talking about her.

____2.   When Don Pedro and Claudio begin to tease Benedick about being in love with Beatrice, Benedick responds by saying

A. he has indigestion.
B. he has grown lovesick.
C. he has a toothache.
D. he has been wounded in a duel.
E. he needs sleep.

____3.   From Dogberry's instructions to his watch, we can conclude that

A. Dogberry is an efficient police officer.
B. Dogberry is smart.
C. Dogberry is a cowardly fool.
D. Dogberry is brave.
E. Dogberry is a good friend of the Prince's.

____4.   When Hero, Margaret, and Ursula tease Beatrice about being in love with Benedick, Beatrice

A. claims to have a toothache.
B. assails them with her wit.
C. claims to be sick.
D. claims to need sleep.
E. says she has indigestion.

____5.   Leonato is impatient with Dogberry and Verges because

A. they don't get to the point of their visit.
B. they come to the point too quickly to make sense.
C. they have already conducted the examination of the prisoners.
D. they want to be invited to the wedding.
E. they have executed the prisoners before he could question them.

Postreading Activity
for
Much Ado About Nothing
Small Group Discussion to Check Comprehension
Act III

Directions: After you've read all of Act III, discuss each of the following questions in small groups briefly. Use the space below each question to note points you may wish to share later. If you need more room, use the back of the page.

1.   How do Hero and Ursula change their speech once they know Beatrice is listening?

2.   How does Beatrice show the audience that the trick has worked?

3.   Which elements of the language of Don Pedro, Claudio, and Leonato let the audience know that their trick has worked on Benedick?

4.   How does the tone of the scene change once Don John comes to see Don Pedro and Claudio?

5.   Why is Beatrice so concerned about Margaret's suggestion to give her some distilled Cardus Benedictus?

6.   What is the principal source of humor in scene v between Leonato and Dogberry?

Postreading Activity
for
Much Ado About Nothing
Critical Thinking Questions
Act III

Directions: To help you develop your understanding of Act III, as your teacher directs you, take time to think about and discuss these questions. The first question is the focus question and is the point of the discussion. Don't be concerned that you may not be able to answer this question at first. Proceed to the exploration questions and then return to the focus question.

Focus Question. If you found yourself in a situation where people were talking about you, how might you react differently from the characters in the play?

Exploration Questions.

1. In what other works of literature have characters been tricked by supposedly overhearing a conversation about them?

2. What kinds of places do we consider ideal for sharing secrets?

3. Based upon what you've seen in the play, what kinds of things do you think happen in the garden of Leonato's house?

4. How does the garden in this play compare with other natural settings in other works of literature?

5. How does your behavior with your friends change when you're in different settings?

6. How does being in the garden or orchards of Leonato's estate affect the actions of Beatrice and Benedick?

Postreading Activity
for
Much Ado About Nothing
Language Exploration:
Sensory Imagery
Act III

In addition to similes, metaphors, personification, apostrophe, and symbol, Shakespeare also uses *sensory imagery*: language that appeals to the senses of sight, touch, taste, smell, and hearing. Because our senses provide direct contact with the world, poets often appeal to these concrete experiences to help convey more abstract ideas. Shakespeare often develops sensory imagery in combination with other figurative language.

Directions: The following passages from Acts I, II, and III are examples of sensory imagery. Working in pairs, small groups, or as your teacher directs, review each passage in the context of the play and decide to which sense (or senses) Shakespeare appeals and what the passage suggests to the reader.

1.   Beatrice mockingly describing Benedick (Act I, scene i):

&

You had musty victual, and he hath holp to eat it: he is a very valiant trencherman; he hath an excellent stomach.

&

2.   Benedick commenting on Don Pedro's praise of Hero being like her father (Act I, scene i):

&

If Signior Leonato be her father, she would not have his head on her shoulders for all Messina, as like him as she is.

&

© 1997 by The Center for Applied Research in Education

3.   Beatrice's retort to Benedick about his face (Act I, scene i):

          ❧

Scratching could not make it worse, and 'twere such a face as yours were.

          ❧

4.   Benedick disdaining marriage to Claudio (Act I, scene i):

          ❧

Is it come to this? In faith, hath not the world one man but he will wear his cap with suspicion? Shall I never see a bachelor of three-score again? Go to, i' faith; an thou wilt needs thrust thy neck into a yoke, wear the print of it and sigh away Sundays.

          ❧

5.   Don John describing his own character to Conrade (Act I, scene iii):

          ❧

In this, though I cannot be said to be a flattering honest man, it must not be denied I am a plain-dealing villain. I am trusted with a muzzle and enfranchised with a clog; therefore I have decreed not to sing in my cage. If I had my mouth, I would bite; if I had my liberty, I would do my liking: in the meantime let me be that I am, and seek not to alter me.

          ❧

6.   Beatrice jokingly describing the perfect man (Act II, scene i):

          ❧

With a good leg and a good foot, uncle, and money enough in his purse, such a man would win any woman in the world, if a' could get her good-will.

          ❧

7. Beatrice describing what she would do with a beardless man (Act II, scene i):

> *What should I do with him? Dress him in my apparel and make him my waiting-gentlewoman? He that hath a beard is more than a youth, and he that hath no beard is less than a man.*

8. Benedick being scornful of Claudio marrying Hero (Act II, scene i):

> *What fashion will you wear the garland of? About your neck, like an usurer's chain? or under your arm, like a lieutenant's scarf? You must wear it one way, for the prince hath got your Hero.*

9. Ursula commenting to Hero on the trick they are about to play on Beatrice (Act III, scene i):

> *The pleasant'st angling is to see the fish*
> *Cut with her golden oars the silver stream,*
> *And greedily devour the treacherous bait.*

10. Don Pedro commenting to Claudio on the change in Benedick's disposition (Act III, scene ii):

> *Nay, that would be as great a soil in the new gloss of your marriage as to show a child his new coat and forbid him to wear it. I will only be bold with Benedick for his company; for, from the crown of his head to the sole of his foot, he is all mirth:*

© 1997 by The Center for Applied Research in Education

Postreading Activity
for
Much Ado About Nothing
Vocabulary in Context
Act III

Directions: In each of the passages below you will find one of the words from the prereading vocabulary list for Act III. Review the definitions given in the prereading vocabulary. Working individually, in pairs, or in small groups as your teacher directs, examine each of the underlined words in the following passages from Act III. For each word, use the appropriate meaning and develop a brief interpretation of the passage within the context of the play.

scene i.

1.   Hero sending Margaret to tell Beatrice that Hero and Ursula are gossiping about how Benedick is in love with Beatrice.

ஃ

> Good Margaret, run thee to the parlor;
> There shalt thou find my cousin Beatrice
> Proposing with the prince and Claudio:
> Whisper her ear and tell her, I and Ursula
> Walk in the orchard and our whole discourse
> Is all of her; say that thou overheard'st us;
> And bid her steal into the <u>pleached</u> bower,
> Where honeysuckles, ripen'd by the sun,
> Forbid the sun to enter; —like favorites,
> Made proud by princes, that advance their pride
> Against that power that bred it: —there will she hide her,
> To listen our purpose.

ஃ

scene ii.

2.   Don John trying to convince Don Pedro and Claudio that Hero is not the honorable and chaste young girl that she appears to be.

129

❧

The word is too good to paint out her wickedness; I say she were worse: think you of a worse, and I will fit her to it. Wonder not till <u>warrant</u>: go but with me to-night, you shall see her chamber-window entered, even the night her wedding-day: if you love her then, to-morrow wed her; but it would better fit your honor to change your mind.

❧

scene iii.

3. Borachio bragging to Conrade about his villainy in discrediting Hero.

❧

sometimes fashioning them like Pharaoh's soldiers in the <u>reechy</u> painting;

❧

4. Borachio bragging to Conrade about his villainy in discrediting Hero.

❧

sometimes like the shaven Hercules in the <u>smirched</u> worm-eaten tapestry, where his cod-piece seems as massy as his club?

❧

scene iv.

5. Beatrice responding to Hero, Margaret, and Ursula teasing her about being in love with Benedick.

❧

O, God help me! God help me! How long have you <u>apprehension</u>?

❧

Vocabulary Review Quiz
for
Much Ado About Nothing
Act III

Directions: For each of the italicized words in the sentences below, determine which letter best reflects the use of the word in this context. Place the letter corresponding to your answer in the space to the left of the item number.

____1.   The *pleached* bower that Hero refers to is

A. a plant in Leonato's garden.
B. a fragrant flower.
C. an arbor of vines or branches.
D. limbs bleached in the sun.
E. a grape arbor.

____2.   As Don John uses *warrant*, he means

A. a paper authorizing arrest.
B. sufficient guilt.
C. insufficient guilt.
D. due process.
E. accusation.

____3.   As Borachio uses *reechy*, he means

A. unclear.
B. rancid.
C. smoky.
D. clear.
E. old.

____4.   As Borachio uses *smirched*, he means

A. unclear.
B. rancid.
C. smoky.
D. clear.
E. smudged.

____5.   As Beatrice uses *apprehension*, she means

      A. knowledge.
      B. understanding.
      C. sagacity.
      D. wisdom.
      E. warrant.

ACT IV

© 1997 by The Center for Applied Research in Education

NAME: _____   DATE: _____

Focusing Activities
for
Much Ado About Nothing
Scenarios for Improvisation
Act IV

Directions: Presented below are locations and situations involving characters. As your teacher directs you, but before reading an individual scene, pretend to be one of the characters and act out the situation. Don't worry about speaking like the characters in Shakespeare's plays, just try to imagine how you would react to the situation and use your own language. Your teacher may give you a few minutes to discuss what you would like to do with the other performers. Your teacher will probably ask you to act out your scene for others in the class. When you finish, your teacher may ask your classmates to discuss what they've seen.

scene i.   *Scene*: The church the day of Hero and Claudio's marriage.

Characters: Claudio, Hero, Leonato.

Situation: Now that Claudio is convinced that Hero is unfaithful, he has vowed to denounce her at the wedding. What does he say and how do Hero and Leonato react?

scene ii.   *Scene*: The jail.

Characters: Dogberry, Borachio, Conrade, Members of the Watch.

Situation: Leonato has ordered Dogberry to question Borachio and Conrade who have been arrested. How does Dogberry manage to question the men and still get at the truth?

Focusing Activities
for
Much Ado About Nothing
Small Group Discussion Questions
Act IV

Directions: Before reading scenes in Act IV, discuss the questions in small groups. You may want to make notes about your discussion so you can share them with classmates or refer to them after you've read the scene.

scene i. Now that Claudio is convinced that Hero is unfaithful, he has vowed to denounce her at the wedding. What does he say and how do Hero and Leonato react?

scene ii. Leonato has ordered Dogberry to question Borachio and Conrade who have been arrested. How does Dogberry manage to question the men and still get at the truth?

NAME: _____   DATE: _____

Focusing Activities
for
Much Ado About Nothing
Speculation Journal
Act IV

Directions: This activity will help you become involved actively with reading the play by helping you to determine a definite purpose for reading. Before you read these scenes in Act IV, take a few minutes to respond in writing to questions below. Don't worry about correct answers here. Use your own experience or what you have read in the play to speculate about what you think will happen. After reading a scene you may find the characters reacted differently than you thought. Don't worry about these differences; just make note of them because you will have opportunities to share these differences in other activities.

scene i.

1. Don John's plot should convince Don Pedro and Claudio that Hero is unfaithful on the evening before their wedding. If you were Claudio, what would you do at the wedding?

2. How do you think Hero and Leonato will react to your plans?

scene ii.

1. Although Leonato has ordered Dogberry to question Borachio and Conrade, how likely is it that they will succeed?

2. What do you think would have to happen for Dogberry to gain a confession from Borachio and Conrade?

After reading Act IV

Now that you have finished reading Act IV, which of your speculations were most like the action of the characters in the play? How do you account for them? Which ones were least like the action of the play? Why do you think you speculated as you did?

Prereading Activity
for
Much Ado About Nothing
Vocabulary
Act IV

Directions: Shakespeare uses the following words in Act IV. The section below provides a brief definition of each word and provides a sentence to illustrate its meaning. You may wish to review the words for a particular scene immediately before reading it.

Definitions.

scene i

1. **particular:** (adj.) private, personal; detailed.
   Example: After swearing the new assistant to secrecy, the scientist then explained his *particular* duties.

2. **counterpoise:** (v.) counterbalance; equalize.
   Example: My nephew is able to *counterpoise* his athletic abilities with strong academic standing.

3. **intemperate:** (adj.) unrestrained, wild.
   Example: Teenagers are often characterized as being *intemperate*.

4. **misgovernment:** (n.) misconduct.
   Example: Once the bank executive was returned from the Grand Cayman Islands, he pleaded no contest to the charges of *misgovernment*.

5. **conjecture:** (n.) speculation.
   Example: Immediately before the murder trial, there was great *conjecture* about the suspect's guilt.

Prereading Activity
for
Much Ado About Nothing
Plot Summaries
Act IV

Directions: To help you better understand and follow Shakespeare's play, read the summary of specific scenes immediately before you begin to read the original. If you get lost during the scene, refer to the summary again.

Act IV, scene i

Don Pedro, Don John, Leonato, Friar Francis, Claudio, Benedick, Hero, Beatrice, and attendants are gathered at the church for the wedding. When Leonato gives Hero's hand to Claudio, he refuses it and charges her with infidelity. Don Pedro confirms what he and Claudio saw at midnight. Hero faints and Don John ushers Don Pedro and Claudio out.

Beatrice is immediately ready to defend her cousin's innocence as is Friar Francis, the priest present to perform the ceremony. Neither Leonato nor Benedick know what to believe. The friar suggests that Leonato proclaim that Hero has died as a result of her shame. Benedick, moved by Beatrice's loyalty to Hero, proclaims his love for her and she for him. When Benedick asks what he can do to prove his love, Beatrice replies that Benedick should kill Claudio. Reluctantly, Benedick agrees.

Act IV, scene ii

At the prison, Dogberry and Verges, the Sexton, and the watchmen prepare to question Borachio and Conrade. They discover that Don John gave Borachio a thousand ducats to help discredit Hero. They also knew how Claudio would refuse Hero in the church. They reveal that Don John has fled and Hero is dead as a result of her shame. Dogberry orders the two men be taken to Leonato.

Class Period:

CHARACTER ASSIGNMENTS FOR ORAL READING GROUPS

Much Ado About Nothing

Session 6: Act IV, scenes i, ii

Characters	*Group 1*	*Group 2*	*Group 3*	*Group 4*
Don Pedro, First Watchman	___	___	___	___
Don John, Verges	___	___	___	___
Leonato, Sexton	___	___	___	___
Friar Francis, Conrade	___	___	___	___
Claudio	___	___	___	___
Benedick, Borachio	___	___	___	___
Hero, Dogberry	___	___	___	___
Beatrice	___	___	___	___

141

NAME: _____   DATE: _____

During-Reading Activity
for
Much Ado About Nothing
Character Diary 6
Act IV, scenes i, ii

Directions: Use the space below to record your character's reactions to the events of the first two scenes in Act IV of *Much Ado About Nothing*. Remember to include a summary of events, explain how your character learned of them, and give your character's reactions to them. If you need additional room, use the back of this sheet.

The Personal Diary of

_____
(character's name)

The church
The day of the wedding

_____
_____
_____
_____
_____
_____
_____

The local jail
The same afternoon

_____
_____
_____
_____
_____
_____
_____

During-Reading Activity
for
Much Ado About Nothing
Viewing Act IV, scene i
Claudio Denounces Hero

Directions: After you've read this scene, viewing a film or video version may help you better understand how the text translates into characters' actions. Although you may want to keep your copy of the play handy, don't be surprised if the actors' script varies from yours. Film scripts often delete or reorder the lines in the play. You may want to note questions you need to ask your teacher afterward. After viewing the scene, take a few minutes to respond to the questions below.

1. How do Claudio's facial expressions and gestures suggest his anger toward Hero even before he formally denounces her?

2. How do Leonato's reactions to Claudio's accusations change during the scene?

3. How do Benedick, Beatrice, and Don John react to Claudio's accusations?

4. How do the actors' facial expressions, tones of voice, and gestures enhance Shakespeare's lines?

During-Reading Activity
for
Much Ado About Nothing
Guide to Character Development: Hero
Act IV

Shakespeare reveals his characters in four ways:

- ❧ through what the characters say to other characters in dialogue;
- ❧ through what the characters reveal about their thoughts through long speeches to the audience called *soliloquies*;
- ❧ through what other characters say about them;
- ❧ through what they do, their actions.

As you read the play, examine the following scenes for what they reveal about Hero's character and fill in the chart briefly using your own words. If you need more room, use the back of the page.

Scene	What Hero says, does, or what others say about her	What this reveals about Hero's character
Act IV, scene i Hero tries to defend herself from Claudio's allegations		
Act IV, scene i Hero faints when Claudio denounces her		

During-Reading Activity
for
Much Ado About Nothing
Guide to Character Development: Beatrice
Act IV

Shakespeare reveals his characters in four ways:

- through what the characters say to other characters in dialogue;
- through what the characters reveal about their thoughts through long speeches to the audience called *soliloquies*;
- through what other characters say about them;
- through what they do, their actions.

As you read the play, examine the following scenes for what they reveal about Beatrice's character and fill in the chart briefly using your own words. If you need more room, use the back of the page.

Scene	*What Beatrice says, does, or what others say about her*	*What this reveals about Beatrice's character*
Act IV, scene i Beatrice refuses to believe Claudio's charges		
Act IV, scene i Beatrice tells Benedick to prove his love for her by killing Claudio		

During-Reading Activity
for
Much Ado About Nothing
Guide to Character Development: Benedick
Act IV

Shakespeare reveals his characters in four ways:

- through what the characters say to other characters in dialogue;
- through what the characters reveal about their thoughts through long speeches to the audience called *soliloquies*;
- through what other characters say about them;
- through what they do, their actions.

As you read the play, examine the following scenes for what they reveal about Benedick's character and fill in the chart briefly using your own words. If you need more room, use the back of the page.

Scene	What Benedick says, does, or what others say about him	What this reveals about Benedick's character
Act IV, scene i Benedick urges Leonato to listen to Friar Francis's advice about Hero pretending to be dead		
Act IV, scene i Benedick offers to do anything to prove his love to Beatrice		

During-Reading Activity
for
Much Ado About Nothing
Guide to Character Development: Claudio
Act IV

Shakespeare reveals his characters in four ways:

 - through what the characters say to other characters in dialogue;
 - through what the characters reveal about their thoughts through long speeches to the audience called *soliloquies*;
 - through what other characters say about them;
 - through what they do, their actions.

As you read the play, examine the following scene for what it reveals about Claudio's character and fill in the chart briefly using your own words. If you need more room, use the back of the page.

Scene	What Claudio says, does, or what others say about him	What this reveals about Claudio's character
Act IV, scene i Claudio denounces Hero at their wedding		

During-Reading Activity
for
Much Ado About Nothing
Guide to Character Development: Don Pedro
Act IV

Shakespeare reveals his characters in four ways:

- through what the characters say to other characters in dialogue;
- through what the characters reveal about their thoughts through long speeches to the audience called *soliloquies*;
- through what other characters say about them;
- through what they do, their actions.

As you read the play, examine the following scene for what it reveals about Don Pedro's character and fill in the chart briefly using your own words. If you need more room, use the back of the page.

Scene	What Don Pedro says, does, or what others say about him	What this reveals about Don Pedro's character
Act IV, scene i Don Pedro supports Claudio's accusations of Hero		

© 1997 by The Center for Applied Research in Education

During-Reading Activity
for
Much Ado About Nothing
Guide to Character Development: Leonato
Act IV

Shakespeare reveals his characters in four ways:

- through what the characters say to other characters in dialogue;
- through what the characters reveal about their thoughts through long speeches to the audience called *soliloquies*;
- through what other characters say about them;
- through what they do, their actions.

As you read the play, examine the following scenes for what they reveal about Leonato's character and fill in the chart briefly using your own words. If you need more room, use the back of the page.

Scene	What Leonato says, does, or what others say about him	What this reveals about Leonato's character
Act IV, scene i Leonato, though horrified at the allegations, turns on Hero		
Act IV, scene i Leonato agrees to follow the Friar's advice		

During-Reading Activity
for
Much Ado About Nothing
Guide to Character Development: Don John
Act IV

Shakespeare reveals his characters in four ways:

- through what the characters say to other characters in dialogue;
- through what the characters reveal about their thoughts through long speeches to the audience called *soliloquies*;
- through what other characters say about them;
- through what they do, their actions.

As you read the play, examine the following scene for what it reveals about Don John's character and fill in the chart briefly using your own words. If you need more room, use the back of the page.

Scene	What Don John says, does, or what others say about him	What this reveals about Don John's character
Act IV, scene i Don John urges that the names of the offenses and the man not be named		

© 1997 by The Center for Applied Research in Education

NAME: _____   DATE: _____

During-Reading Activity
for
Much Ado About Nothing
Guide to Character Development: Borachio
Act IV

Shakespeare reveals his characters in four ways:

- through what the characters say to other characters in dialogue;
- through what the characters reveal about their thoughts through long speeches to the audience called *soliloquies*;
- through what other characters say about them;
- through what they do, their actions.

As you read the play, examine the following scene for what it reveals about Borachio's character and fill in the chart briefly using your own words. If you need more room, use the back of the page.

Scene	*What Borachio says, does, or what others say about him*	*What this reveals about Borachio's character*
Act IV, scene ii The Sexton reveals that Don John has fled and that Hero was denounced like Borachio and Conrade discussed		

During-Reading Activity
for
Much Ado About Nothing
Guide to Character Development: Dogberry
Act IV

Shakespeare reveals his characters in four ways:

- through what the characters say to other characters in dialogue;
- through what the characters reveal about their thoughts through long speeches to the audience called *soliloquies*;
- through what other characters say about them;
- through what they do, their actions.

As you read the play, examine the following scene for what it reveals about Dogberry's character and fill in the chart briefly using your own words. If you need more room, use the back of the page.

Scene	What Dogberry says, does, or what others say about him	What this reveals about Dogberry's character
Act IV, scene ii The Sexton has to direct Dogberry on how to conduct the examination of Borachio and Conrade		

Postreading Activity
for
Much Ado About Nothing
Comprehension Check
Act IV

Directions: After you've read all of Act IV, use the following questions to check how well you've understood what you've read. For each question, select the most appropriate answer from the choices listed below it. Place the letter corresponding to your answer in the space to the left of the item number.

_____1.   What business does Benedick wish to discuss with Friar Francis at the beginning of Act IV, scene i?

A. He wishes to pay for Claudio's wedding.
B. He wishes to join the monastery.
C. He needs to make arrangements to marry Beatrice.
D. He wishes to make arrangements for Don Pedro to marry Beatrice.
E. He needs to make his confession.

_____2.   Throughout Claudio's accusations of Hero, he

A. compares her to rotten apples.
B. compares her to pagan deities.
C. points out that her modesty is not what it seems.
D. calls her vile names.
E. is willing to forgive her.

_____3.   At the end of the scene, Friar Francis suggests that

A. Hero join a convent.
B. Hero beg Claudio's forgiveness.
C. Hero pretend to be dead.
D. Hero change her name.
E. Hero leave the country.

_____4.   What promise does Benedick make to prove his love for Beatrice?

A. To carry her token into war.
B. To give her the most valuable gem he can find.
C. To challenge Claudio to a duel.
D. To kill Claudio.
E. To kill Don Pedro.

_____5.   Which character is really responsible for gaining the truth of what Borachio and Conrade have done in Act IV, scene ii?

A. Dogberry
B. Borachio
C. Conrade
D. The Sexton
E. The members of the watch

NAME: _____   DATE: _____

Postreading Activity
for
Much Ado About Nothing
Small Group Discussion to Check Comprehension
Act IV

Directions: After you've read all of Act IV, discuss each of the following questions in small groups briefly. Use the space below each question to note points you may wish to share later. If you need more room, use the back of the page.

1. How does the language change throughout the scene to reflect the shift in tone from joyous celebration to despair?

2. What kinds of comparisons does Claudio use in making his accusations about Hero's character?

3. What plan does Friar Francis propose to help regain Hero's reputation?

4. How does Claudio's denunciation of Hero affect the relationship between Beatrice and Benedick?

5. What enables the bumbling Dogberry to succeed in getting the truth from Borachio and Conrade?

Postreading Activity
for
Much Ado About Nothing
Critical Thinking Questions
Act IV

Directions: To help you develop your understanding of Act IV, as your teacher directs you, take time to think about and discuss these questions. The first question is the focus question and is the point of the discussion. Don't be concerned that you may not be able to answer this question at first. Proceed to the exploration questions and then return to the focus question.

Focus Question. If you were Claudio or Leonato, why would you or wouldn't you be willing to believe Claudio's accusations of Hero's character?

Exploration Questions.

1. In what other works of literature are principal characters accused falsely?

2. What kinds of activities do we expect to happen in churches?

3. What convinces Leonato of the truth behind Claudio's allegations?

4. How does the accusation scene in this play contrast with scenes in other works of literature where someone is accused?

5. What types of evidence would you need to be convinced that Claudio's accusations were true?

6. How does making an accusation in church affect its seriousness?

Postreading Activity
for
Much Ado About Nothing
Language Exploration:
Apostrophe
Act IV

You're walking down the hallway after school and you pass a classmate. You turn and call out, "Kim, can I speak to you?" Kim doesn't hear you and continues on her way. You mutter, "That's O.K., Kim, it wasn't very important anyway."

In the first line of dialogue, you addressed Kim directly. In the second, although Kim was no longer within earshot, you pretended she was present and aired your feelings.

Poets also use the device of having a character speak to a person or an abstract idea even though the person or idea isn't or can't be present. This particular device is called *apostrophe*. Consider the following examples:

ॐ

Death, be not proud.
Rose, where'd you get that red?
Twinkle, twinkle little star,
How I wonder what you are.

ॐ

In the first example, the speaker addresses Death and tells it to not be proud. This suggests that the speaker doesn't fear death. The second example allows the speaker to address a flower and speculate how it came to be red. The nursery rhyme in the third example lets the speaker address a star and contemplate it.

Directions: The following lines contain examples of apostrophe taken from Acts I, II, III, and IV. Working in pairs, small groups, or as your teacher directs, review each passage in the context of the play to determine who or what is addressed, and what the apostrophe suggests to the reader.

1.   Claudio, Leonato, and Don Pedro convince Benedick that Beatrice is hopelessly in love with him (Act II, scene iii):

ॐ

Then down upon her knees she falls, weeps, sobs, beats her
heart, tears her hair, prays, curses; 'O sweet Benedick! God
give me patience!'

ॐ

157

2. After Ursula, Margaret, and Hero convince Beatrice that Benedick is hopelessly in love with her, she emerges from her hiding place and comments (Act III, scene i):

    ❧

    > *No glory lives behind the back of such*
    > *And, Benedick, love on; I will requite thee,*
    > *Taming my wild heart to thy loving hand:*
    > *If thou dost love, my kindness shall incite thee*
    > *To bind our loves up in a holy band;*
    > *For others say thou dost deserve, and I*
    > *Believe it better than reportingly.*

    ❧

3. Don Pedro, Claudio, and Don John go to observe Hero being unfaithful (Act III, scene ii):

    ❧

    > <u>Don Pedro:</u> *O day untowardly turned!*
    > <u>Claudio:</u> *O mischief strangely thwarting!*
    > <u>Don John:</u> *O plague right well prevented! So will you say,*
    > *when you have seen the sequel.*

    ❧

4. Claudio denouncing Hero (Act IV, scene i):

    ❧

    > *Behold how like a maid she blushes here!*
    > *O, what authority and show of truth*
    > *Can cunning sin cover itself withal!*
    > *Comes not that blood as modest evidence*
    > *To witness simple virtue?*

    ❧

5. Leonato lamenting Hero's fallen reputation (Act IV, scene i):

    ❧

    > *O Fate! take not away thy heavy hand.*
    > *Death is the fairest cover for her shame*
    > *That may be wish'd for.*

    ❧

NAME: _____   DATE: _____

Postreading Activity
for
Much Ado About Nothing
Vocabulary in Context
Act IV

Directions: In each of the passages below you will find one of the words from the prereading vocabulary list for Act IV. Review the definitions given in the prereading vocabulary. Working individually, in pairs, or in small groups as your teacher directs, examine each of the underlined words in the following passages from Act IV. For each word, use the appropriate meaning and develop a brief interpretation of the passage within the context of the play.

scene i.

1. Leonato speaking to Friar Francis to perform a simple marriage ceremony:

    ❧

    > Come, Friar Francis, be brief; only to the plain form
    > of marriage, and you shall recount their <u>particular</u> duties
    > afterwards.

    ❧

2. Claudio's reply to Leonato giving Hero in marriage:

    ❧

    > And what have I to give you back, whose worth
    > May <u>counterpoise</u> this rich and precious gift?

    ❧

3. Claudio denouncing Hero as unchaste:

    ❧

    > But you are more <u>intemperate</u> in your blood
    > Than Venus, or those pamper'd animals
    > That rage in savage sensuality.

    ❧

4.   Don John adding to the evidence to discredit Hero:

❧

> Fie, fie! they are not to be named, my lord,
> Not to be spoke of;
> There is not chastity enough in language
> Without offense to utter them. Thus, pretty lady,
> I am sorry for thy much <u>misgovernment</u>.

❧

5.   Claudio denouncing Hero as unchaste:

❧

> O Hero, what a Hero hadst thou been,
> If half thy outward graces had been placed
> About thy thoughts and counsels of thy heart!
> But fare thee well, most foul, most fair! Farewell,
> Thou pure impiety and impious purity!
> For thee I'll lock up all the gates of love,
> And on my eyelids shall <u>conjecture</u> hang,
> To turn all beauty into thoughts of harm,
> And never shall it more be gracious.

❧

NAME: _____   DATE: _____

Vocabulary Review Quiz
for
Much Ado About Nothing
Act IV

Directions: For each of the italicized words in the sentences below, determine which letter best reflects the use of the word in this context. Place the letter corresponding to your answer in the space to the left of the item number.

_____1.   As Leonato uses *particular* in Act IV, scene i, he means

    A. specific.
    B. private or personal.
    C. individual.
    D. religious.
    E. ceremonial.

_____2.   When Claudio uses *counterpoise*, he means

    A. address directly.
    B. address indirectly.
    C. praise.
    D. exploit.
    E. counterbalance.

_____3.   When Claudio suggests that Hero is *intemperate*, he means that she has

    A. behaved sensibly.
    B. behaved unrestrainedly.
    C. behaved childishly.
    D. become insane.
    E. become unrecognizable.

_____4.   When Don John uses *misgovernment*, he means

    A. illegal use of power.
    B. treason.
    C. misconduct.
    D. misappropriation.
    E. missive.

_____5. When Claudio says "And on my eyelids shall *conjecture* hang," he means that he will look upon Hero with

A. contempt.
B. suspicion.
C. forgiveness.
D. sorrow.
E. evil.

ACT V

© 1997 by The Center for Applied Research in Education

NAME: _____   DATE: _____

Focusing Activities
for
Much Ado About Nothing
Scenarios for Improvisation
Act V

Directions: Presented below are locations and situations involving characters. As your teacher directs you, but before reading an individual scene, pretend to be one of the characters and act out the situation. Don't worry about speaking like characters in Shakespeare's plays, just try to imagine how you would react to the situation and use your own language. Your teacher may give you a few minutes to discuss what you would like to do with the other performers. Your teacher will probably ask you to act out your scene for others in the class. When you finish, your teacher may ask your classmates to discuss what they've seen.

scene i.   *Scene:* In front of Leonato's house.

Characters: Leonato, Antonio, Claudio, Don Pedro.

Situation: Leonato and Antonio are angry with Claudio and Don Pedro for denouncing Hero at the wedding. When they meet in front of the house, what do they say to each other?

scene ii.   *Scene:* Leonato's orchard.

Characters: Benedick and Beatrice.

Situation: Benedick tries to act the part of the lover to Beatrice. What does he say and how does she respond?

scene iii.   *Scene:* The churchyard.

Characters: Claudio and Don Pedro.

Situation: Leonato has ordered Claudio to go to the family tomb, where Claudio believes Hero has been buried, and publish an epitaph so all the town will know that she was accused falsely. What does Claudio say in his epitaph and how does he present it?

scene iv.   *Scene:* The church the day of the wedding between Claudio and Leonato's "niece."

Characters: Claudio, Leonato, Hero (in disguise).

Situation: Claudio has agreed to marry Leonato's "niece." How does Leonato go about presenting the bride, and how does Claudio react both before he knows the true identity of his bride and afterward?

Focusing Activities
for
Much Ado About Nothing
Small Group Discussion Questions
Act V

Directions: Before reading scenes in Act V, discuss the questions in small groups. You may want to make notes about your discussion so you can share them with classmates or refer to them after you've read the scene.

scene i. Leonato and Antonio are angry with Claudio and Don Pedro for denouncing Hero at the wedding. When they meet in front of Leonato's house, what do you think they will say to each other?

scene ii. Now that Benedick and Beatrice have declared their love for each other, they must try to act like lovers. What might Benedick say and how might Beatrice respond?

scene iii. Leonato has ordered Claudio to go to the family tomb, where Claudio believes Hero has been buried, and publish an epitaph so all the town will know that she was accused falsely. What do you think Claudio might say and how might he present it?

scene iv. Claudio has agreed to marry Leonato's "niece." How might Leonato go about presenting the bride, and how might Claudio react both before he knows the true identity of his bride and afterward?

NAME: _____   DATE: _____

Focusing Activities
for
Much Ado About Nothing
Speculation Journal
Act V

Directions: This activity will help you become involved actively with reading the play by helping you to determine a definite purpose for reading. Before you read these scenes in Act V, take a few minutes to respond in writing to the questions below. Don't worry about correct answers here. Use your own experience or what you have read in the play to speculate about what you think will happen. After reading a scene you may find that the characters reacted differently than you thought. Don't worry about these differences; just make note of them because you will have opportunities to share these differences in other activities.

scene i.

1.   Because Claudio and Don Pedro denounced Hero, ruining her reputation, what do you think the older men might do when they encounter Don Pedro and Claudio later the same day?

2.   The men have tricked Benedick into believing that Beatrice loves him. Similarly, the women have tricked Beatrice into believing that Benedick is in love with her. How might each person acknowledge the love of the other at the wedding?

scene ii.   Once Benedick and Beatrice have declared their love for each other, what might each do in trying to play the role of a person madly in love?

167

scene iii.   If you were Claudio, what would you include in the epitaph that you have been ordered to place on Hero's tomb?

scene iv.   If you were Leonato, how would you go about presenting your "niece," who looks a great deal like Hero, to Claudio at the wedding so you would not give away the surprise too soon?

**After
reading
Act V**   Now that you have finished reading Act V, which of your speculations were most like the action of the characters in the play? How do you account for them? Which ones were least like the action of the play? Why do you think you speculated as you did?

NAME: _____   DATE: _____

Prereading Activity
for
Much Ado About Nothing
Vocabulary
Act V

Directions: Shakespeare uses the following words in Act V. The section below provides a brief definition of each word and provides a sentence to illustrate its meaning. You may wish to review the words for a particular scene immediately before reading it.

Definitions.
scene i.

1. **advertisement:** (n.) general knowledge or publication of an event; gossip.

    Example: Because of the *advertisement* about the crime, the judge ruled the trial should be heard in another part of the state.

2. **dissembler:** (n.) deceiver, hypocrite.

    Example: People who espouse one belief but practice another are often viewed as *dissemblers*.

3. **foining:** (adj.) thrusting and slashing; wounding with a sharp, pointed object.

    Example: While playing pirate, the two boys used their wooden swords in *foining* strokes as they made their imaginary enemies walk the plank.

4. **invention:** (n.) imagination.

    Example: Because Claudio was possessive of Hero's love, his *invention* was able to see guilt when there wasn't any.

5. **countenance:** (n.) face.

    Example: Throughout the play, many characters are accused of being in love because of the expressions on their *countenances*.

169

Prereading Activity
for
Much Ado About Nothing
Plot Summaries
Act V

Directions: To help you better understand and follow *Much Ado About Nothing*, read the summary of a specific scene before you begin to read it. If you get lost during the scene, you can refer to the summary.

Act V, scene i

The street in front of Leonato's house. Antonio has been trying to comfort his brother. When Don Pedro and Claudio appear, the two older men try to provoke them into a fight. Benedick joins them and attempts to challenge Claudio. Claudio, however, refuses to take Benedick seriously and continues to jest with him. Benedick becomes angry and leaves, vowing to duel with Claudio. Claudio and Don Pedro realize that Benedick is serious. The two prisoners are brought before Leonato and confess their part in the plot against Hero. Don Pedro and Claudio are remorseful and contrite when they know the truth. To make amends, Claudio agrees to Leonato's unusual offer. Claudio should marry Leonato's "niece," who just happens to look a great deal like Hero, the next day. Claudio agrees.

Act V, scene ii

In Leonato's orchard, Benedick attempts to behave like a real lover. While he's trying to write a sonnet praising Beatrice's beauty, Beatrice interrupts. Even though they have both acknowledged their mutual love, they can't resist matching wits with each other. Ursula informs them that Hero has had her reputation restored and the group goes to Leonato's house to learn the details.

Act V, scene iii

At the churchyard, a repentant Claudio and Don Pedro place a memorial on the family tomb where they believe Hero has been buried. Claudio vows to perform rites yearly in Hero's memory. He and Don Pedro then go to dress for the wedding.

Act V, scene iv

A room in Leonato's house, with Leonato, Antonio, Benedick, Beatrice, Margaret, Ursula, Friar Francis, and Hero (disguised as Leonato's "niece"). While they wait for Claudio and Don Pedro, Benedick arranges to marry Beatrice. When Hero is presented to Claudio, she removes her disguise and explains that she only "died" when her reputation was discredited. Benedick and Beatrice discover their mutual

© 1997 by The Center for Applied Research in Education

mistake in thinking that they were only returning the passionate love of the other. However, both are satisfied with the outcome and Benedick calls for a dance before the marriage ceremony. A messenger arrives and informs the company that Don John has been caught and is being returned to Messina under guard.

Class Period:

CHARACTER ASSIGNMENTS FOR ORAL READING GROUPS

Much Ado About Nothing

Session 7: Act V, scenes i, ii

Characters	_Group 1_	_Group 2_	_Group 3_	_Group 4_
Leonato	_____	_____	_____	_____
Antonio	_____	_____	_____	_____
Don Pedro	_____	_____	_____	_____
Claudio	_____	_____	_____	_____
Benedick	_____	_____	_____	_____
Dogberry, Beatrice	_____	_____	_____	_____
Verges, Margaret	_____	_____	_____	_____
Borachio, Benedick	_____	_____	_____	_____

Class Period:

CHARACTER ASSIGNMENTS FOR ORAL READING GROUPS

Much Ado About Nothing

Session 8: Act V, scenes iii, iv

Characters	_Group 1_	_Group 2_	_Group 3_	_Group 4_
Don Pedro	_____	_____	_____	_____
Claudio	_____	_____	_____	_____
Balthazar, Friar Francis, Messenger	_____	_____	_____	_____
Leonato	_____	_____	_____	_____
Antonio	_____	_____	_____	_____
Benedick	_____	_____	_____	_____
Hero	_____	_____	_____	_____
Beatrice	_____	_____	_____	_____

During-Reading Activity
for
Much Ado About Nothing
Character Diary 7
Act V, scenes i, ii

Directions: Use the space below to record your character's reactions to the first two scenes in Act V of *Much Ado About Nothing*. Remember to include a summary of events, explain how your character learned of them, and give your character's reactions to them. Because this act has four scenes, you may wish to record your character's entries as you read each scene. If you need additional room, use the back of this sheet.

The Personal Diary of

_____
(character's name)

A street in front of Leonato's house
The afternoon following Claudio's denunciation of Hero

_____
_____
_____
_____
_____
_____

Leonato's garden
The same afternoon

_____
_____
_____
_____
_____
_____
_____

NAME: _____   DATE: _____

During-Reading Activity
for
Much Ado About Nothing
Character Diary 8
Act V, scenes iii, iv

Directions: Use the space below to record your character's reactions to the final two scenes in Act V of *Much Ado About Nothing*. Remember to include a summary of events, explain how your character learned of them, and give your character's reactions to them. Because this act has four scenes, you may wish to record your character's entries as you read each scene. If you need additional room, use the back of this sheet.

The Personal Diary of

_____
(character's name)

The churchyard before Leonato's family tomb
That night

_____
_____
_____
_____
_____
_____

The church
The next morning

_____
_____
_____
_____
_____
_____
_____

During-Reading Activity
for
Much Ado About Nothing

Viewing Act V, scenes iii, iv
Claudio Mourns Hero and Then Marries Leonato's "Niece"

Directions: After you've read these scenes, viewing a film or video version may help you better understand how the text translates into characters' actions. Although you may want to keep your copy of the play handy, don't be surprised if the actors' script varies from yours. Film scripts often delete or reorder the lines in the play. You may want to note questions you need to ask your teacher afterward. After viewing the scene, take a few minutes to respond to the questions below.

1.   How do the setting and lighting enhance Claudio's sorrow for what he's done to Hero's reputation?

2.   What is the mood among Leonato's family for the wedding, prior to the arrival of Claudio and Don Pedro?

3.   Before Claudio sees his bride's face, what is his mood and manner? How does it change once he knows the bride is Hero?

4.   How do the actors' facial expressions, tones of voice, and gestures enhance Shakespeare's lines?

NAME: _____   DATE: _____

During-Reading Activity
for
Much Ado About Nothing
Guide to Character Development: Hero
Act V

Shakespeare reveals his characters in four ways:

- ❧ through what the characters say to other characters in dialogue;
- ❧ through what the characters reveal about their thoughts through long speeches to the audience called *soliloquies*;
- ❧ through what other characters say about them;
- ❧ through what they do, their actions.

As you read the play, examine the following scene for what it reveals about Hero's character and fill in the chart briefly using your own words. If you need more room, use the back of the page.

Scene	What Hero says, does, or what others say about her	What this reveals about Hero's character
Act V, scene iv Hero reveals her true identity to Claudio		

During-Reading Activity
for
Much Ado About Nothing
Guide to Character Development: Beatrice
Act V

Shakespeare reveals his characters in four ways:

- through what the characters say to other characters in dialogue;
- through what the characters reveal about their thoughts through long speeches to the audience called *soliloquies*;
- through what other characters say about them;
- through what they do, their actions.

As you read the play, examine the following scenes for what they reveal about Beatrice's character and fill in the chart briefly using your own words. If you need more room, use the back of the page.

Scene	*What Beatrice says, does, or what others say about her*	*What this reveals about Beatrice's character*
Act V, scene ii Beatrice encounters Benedick in the garden where he's trying to write poetry		
Act V, scene iv Beatrice willingly goes along with the masquerade during the wedding		
Act V, scene iv Beatrice agrees to marry Benedick although both were tricked		

During-Reading Activity
for
Much Ado About Nothing
Guide to Character Development: Benedick
Act V

Shakespeare reveals his characters in four ways:

- ❧ through what the characters say to other characters in dialogue;
- ❧ through what the characters reveal about their thoughts through long speeches to the audience called *soliloquies*;
- ❧ through what other characters say about them;
- ❧ through what they do, their actions.

As you read the play, examine the following scenes for what they reveal about Benedick's character and fill in the chart briefly using your own words. If you need more room, use the back of the page.

© 1997 by The Center for Applied Research in Education

Scene	What Benedick says, does, or what others say about him	What this reveals about Benedick's character
Act V, scene i Benedick tries to draw Claudio into a duel		
Act V, scene i Claudio and Don Pedro believe Benedick is jesting		
Act V, scene ii Benedick tries to write Beatrice a love poem		
Act V, scene ii Beatrice interrupts Benedick while he tries to write		

During-Reading Activity
for
Much Ado About Nothing
Guide to Character Development: Claudio
Act V

Shakespeare reveals his characters in four ways:

- through what the characters say to other characters in dialogue;
- through what the characters reveal about their thoughts through long speeches to the audience called *soliloquies*;
- through what other characters say about them;
- through what they do, their actions.

As you read the play, examine the following scenes for what they reveal about Claudio's character and fill in the chart briefly using your own words. If you need more room, use the back of the page.

Scene	*What Claudio says, does, or what others say about him*	*What this reveals about Claudio's character*
Act V, scene i Claudio and Don Pedro encounter Leonato and Antonio on the street but refuse to fight the older men		
Act V, scene i Leonato informs Claudio that Hero has died as a result of being denounced		

© 1997 by The Center for Applied Research in Education

Scene	*What Claudio says, does, or what others say about him*	*What this reveals about Claudio's character*
Act V, scene i Claudio learns that he accused Hero falsely and begs Leonato's forgiveness by offering to do anything Leonato asks		
Act V, scene iii Claudio posts the epitaph and mourns at Hero's tomb		
Act V, scene iv Claudio agrees to marry Leonato's "niece"		

During-Reading Activity
for
Much Ado About Nothing
Guide to Character Development: Don Pedro
Act V

Shakespeare reveals his characters in four ways:

- through what the characters say to other characters in dialogue;
- through what the characters reveal about their thoughts through long speeches to the audience called *soliloquies*;
- through what other characters say about them;
- through what they do, their actions.

As you read the play, examine the following scenes for what they reveal about Don Pedro's character and fill in the chart briefly using your own words. If you need more room, use the back of the page.

Scene	*What Don Pedro says, does, or what others say about him*	*What this reveals about Don Pedro's character*
Act V, scene i Don Pedro refuses to fight either Leonato or Antonio		
Act V, scene i Don Pedro believes that Benedick is jesting when he tries to pick a fight with Claudio		
Act V, scene i Don Pedro agrees to accompany Claudio to Hero's tomb		

NAME: _____   DATE: _____

During-Reading Activity
for
Much Ado About Nothing
Guide to Character Development: Leonato
Act I

Shakespeare reveals his characters in four ways:

- through what the characters say to other characters in dialogue;
- through what the characters reveal about their thoughts through long speeches to the audience called *soliloquies*;
- through what other characters say about them;
- through what they do, their actions.

As you read the play, examine the following scenes for what they reveal about Leonato's character and fill in the chart briefly using your own words. If you need more room, use the back of the page.

Scene	*What Leonato says, does, or what others say about him*	*What this reveals about Leonato's character*
Act V, scene i Leonato attempts to start a fight with Don Pedro and Claudio		
Act V, scene i Leonato imposes his punishment on Claudio: to go to the tomb and publish the epitaph saying she was innocent, and to agree to marry his "niece"		
Act V, scene iv Leonato has Antonio function as father of the bride		

During-Reading Activity
for
Much Ado About Nothing
Guide to Character Development: Borachio
Act V

Shakespeare reveals his characters in four ways:

- through what the characters say to other characters in dialogue;
- through what the characters reveal about their thoughts through long speeches to the audience called *soliloquies*;
- through what other characters say about them;
- through what they do, their actions.

As you read the play, examine the following scene for what it reveals about Borachio's character and fill in the chart briefly using your own words. If you need more room, use the back of the page.

Scene	*What Borachio says, does, or what others say about him*	*What this reveals about Borachio's character*
Act V, scene i Borachio confesses to his part in the false accusation of Hero		

© 1997 by The Center for Applied Research in Education

NAME: _____   DATE: _____

During-Reading Activity
for
Much Ado About Nothing
Guide to Character Development: Dogberry
Act V

Shakespeare reveals his characters in four ways:

- through what the characters say to other characters in dialogue;
- through what the characters reveal about their thoughts through long speeches to the audience called *soliloquies*;
- through what other characters say about them;
- through what they do, their actions.

As you read the play, examine the following scenes for what they reveal about Dogberry's character and fill in the chart briefly using your own words. If you need more room, use the back of the page.

Scene	What Dogberry says, does, or what others say about him	What this reveals about Dogberry's character
Act V, scene ii Dogberry bungles the examination of Borachio and Conrade		
Act V, scene ii Dogberry and his men bring Borachio to Leonato		

Postreading Activity
for
Much Ado About Nothing
Comprehension Check
Act V

Directions: After you've read all of Act V, use the following questions to check how well you've understood what you've read. For each question, select the most appropriate answer from the choices listed below it. Place the letter corresponding to your answer in the space to the left of the item number.

____1.   When Leonato informs Claudio that Hero has died as a result of being wrongfully denounced, Claudio

  A. offers to go on a crusade as penance.
  B. offers to become a monk.
  C. offers to build a church in her memory.
  D. offers to do whatever Leonato asks.
  E. offers to do whatever Don Pedro asks.

____2.   When Benedick tries to pick a fight with Claudio,

  A. Claudio draws his sword and kills Benedick in the street.
  B. Claudio agrees to a duel the next morning at sunrise.
  C. Don Pedro and Claudio begin to fight Benedick.
  D. neither Don Pedro nor Claudio believes Benedick is serious.
  E. Don Pedro breaks up the fight.

____3.   When Beatrice learns that Benedick has not yet killed Claudio, she

  A. becomes angry and leaves.
  B. begins to deride Benedick and threaten not to kiss him.
  C. takes Benedick's sword and starts after Claudio herself.
  D. breaks off with Benedick.
  E. threatens to get Don John to help her kill Claudio.

____4.   In the churchyard before Hero's tomb,

  A. Claudio makes his confession to Friar Francis.
  B. Claudio tries to kill himself.
  C. Claudio posts an epitaph restoring Hero's reputation.
  D. Claudio sings a sad ballad of Hero's life.
  E. Claudio offers to enter a monastery.

_____5. So that the identity of Hero will not be immediately apparent to Claudio,

A. all the women in the wedding party wear masks or veils.
B. all the women are disguised as nuns.
C. none of the women are present.
D. the bride is hidden behind a screen.
E. everyone in the wedding party is required to wear a mask.

Postreading Activity
for
Much Ado About Nothing
Small Group Discussion to Check Comprehension
Act V

Directions: After you've read all of Act V, discuss each of the following questions in small groups briefly. Use the space below each question to note points you may wish to share later. If you need more room, use the back of the page.

1. Why are Don Pedro and Claudio unwilling to fight Leonato, Antonio, and Benedick?

2. Once Claudio learns that he has denounced Hero wrongfully and caused her death, why does he offer to submit to any punishment Leonato can fashion?

3. In scene ii, why do Benedick and Beatrice seem to be such comic lovers?

4. How does the masking of the women in the wedding party affect the overall mood of scene iv?

5. How does the wedding in Act V, scene iv differ from the wedding in Act IV, scene i?

Postreading Activity
for
Much Ado About Nothing
Critical Thinking Questions
Act V

Directions: To help you develop your understanding of Act V, as your teacher directs you, take time to think about and discuss these questions. The first question is the focus question and is the point of the discussion. Don't be concerned that you may not be able to answer this question at first. Proceed to the exploration questions and then return to the focus question.

Focus Question. Given the serious nature of marriage, why do both the characters in the play as well as the members of the audience celebrate Claudio's wedding at the end of *Much Ado About Nothing*?

Exploration Questions.

1. What other works of literature or art end with a wedding?

2. How do you feel about arranged marriages?

3. How does the arranged nature and the wearing of masks or veils affect the tone at the beginning of scene iv?

4. How does the wedding at the end of *Much Ado About Nothing* differ from other weddings that end other works of literature or art?

5. What circumstances would need to exist to have a somber wedding, like the one at the beginning of scene iv, in a contemporary setting?

6. If you were Claudio, why would or wouldn't you be willing to consent to marry someone you hadn't seen?

Postreading Activity
for
Much Ado About Nothing
Language Exploration:
Symbol
Act V

When we use a word, object, or image to represent another idea or concept, it becomes a *symbol*. For example, the American flag is a symbol of our country and its democratic form of government. Another example would be when people drive luxury automobiles or wear expensive watches as symbols to show that they have enough wealth to afford these items.

In Act I, scene i, Beatrice derides Benedick's character with the following statement about his lack of wit:

❧

In our last conflict four of his five wits went halting off,
and now is the whole man governed with one; so that if he
have wit enough to keep himself warm, let him bear it for a
difference between himself and his horse.

❧

Directions: The following lines from Acts I through IV contain symbols. Working in pairs, small groups, or as your teacher directs, review each passage in the context of the play and decide what each symbol suggests to the reader.

1.   Don Pedro's observation in response to Benedick's derision of marriage (Act I, scene i):

❧

In time the savage bull doth bear the yoke.

❧

2.   Don Pedro continuing to counter Benedick's derision of marriage (Act I, scene i):

❧

Nay, if Cupid have not spent all his quiver in Venice,
thou wilt quake for this shortly.

❧

3. Benedick explaining to Don Pedro that Claudio believes the Prince has wooed Hero for himself (Act II, scene i):

2a

The flat transgression of a schoolboy, who, being overjoyed
with finding a birds' nest, shows it his companion, and he
steals it.

2a

4. Benedick protesting the idea that he loves Beatrice (Act II, scene i):

2a

I would not marry her, though she were endowed with all
that Adam had left him before he transgressed:

2a

5. Beatrice coyly turning down Don Pedro's offer of marriage (Act II, scene i):

2a

No, my lord, unless I might have another for working-days:
your grace is too costly to wear every day.

2a

6. Don Pedro vowing to see Benedick and Beatrice married (Act II, scene i):

2a

I will in the interim undertake one of Hercules' labors;
which is, to bring Signior Benedick and the Lady Beatrice
into a mountain of the one with the other.

2a

7. Benedick rationalizing his change of feelings for Beatrice (Act II, scene iii):

&

But doth not the appetite alter. A man loves the meat in his youth that he cannot endure in his age.

&

8. Claudio commenting to Don John about the success of their tricks upon Benedick and Beatrice (Act III, scene ii):

&

'Tis even so. Hero and Margaret have by this played their parts with Beatrice; and then the two bears will not bite one another when they meet.

&

9. Claudio refusing to take Hero from her father (Act IV, scene i):

&

Give not this rotten orange to your friend, She's but the sign and semblance of her honor.

&

10. Friar Francis commenting upon his observations of Hero during Claudio's denunciation of her (Act IV, scene i):

&

By noting of the lady I have mark'd A thousand blushing apparitions To start into her face, a thousand innocent shames.

&

Postreading Activity
for
Much Ado About Nothing
Language Exploration Review Quiz

Directions: Now that you've discussed all the Language Exploration Activities, use the following questions to check how well you can apply what you learned to new selections. For each question, select the most appropriate answer from the choices listed below it. Place the letter corresponding to your answer in the space to the left of the item number.

____1.   The following line is an example of which figurative device?

(Benedick addressing Beatrice; Act I, scene i)

ا

Well, you are a rare parrot-teacher.

ا

A. Simile
B. Metaphor
C. Symbol
D. Apostrophe
E. Irony

____2.   The underlined lines are examples of which figurative device?

(Benedick deriding marriage; Act I, scene i)

ا

With anger, with sickness, or with hunger, my lord, not with love: <u>prove that ever I lose more blood with love than I will get again with drinking</u>, pick out mine eyes with a ballad-maker's pen and hang me up at the door of a brothel-house for the sign of blind Cupid.

ا

A. Simile
B. Metaphor
C. Symbol
D. Apostrophe
E. Sensory imagery

____3. The underlined words in the following line are an example of which figurative device?

(Don Pedro responding to Claudio's request to make a long declaration of Claudio's love to Hero; Act I, scene i)

ૐ

What need the bridge much broader than the flood?

ૐ

A. Simile
B. Metaphor
C. Symbol
D. Apostrophe
E. Personification

____4. The underlined words in the following lines are an example of which figurative device?

(Don John describing Conrade's character according to belief in astrology; Act I, scene iii)

ૐ

I wonder that thou, being, as thou sayest thou art,
born under Saturn, goest about to apply a moral medicine
to a mortifying mischief.

ૐ

A. Simile
B. Metaphor
C. Symbol
D. Apostrophe
E. Irony

____5. The following lines are an example of which figurative device?

(Beatrice describing Don John; Act II, scene i)

ૐ

How tartly that gentleman looks! I never can see him
but I am heart-burned an hour after.

ૐ

A. Simile
B. Metaphor
C. Symbol
D. Apostrophe
E. Sensory imagery

© 1997 by The Center for Applied Research in Education

_____6.   The underlined words in the following lines are an example of which figurative device?

(Beatrice entertaining Leonato with her wit; Act II, scene i)

ﾞﾑ

No, but to the gate; and there will the devil meet me, *like an old cuckold*, with horns on his head, and say 'Get you to heaven, Beatrice, get you to heaven ; here's no place for you maids':

ﾞﾑ

A. Verbal irony
B. Simile
C. Personification
D. Irony of situation
E. Apostrophe

_____7.   Which sense does the following line appeal to?

(Benedick describing Beatrice; Act II, scene i)

ﾞﾑ

She speaks poniards, and every word stabs. If her breath were as terrible as her terminations, there were no living near her; *she would infect to the north star*.

ﾞﾑ

A. Sight
B. Sound
C. Taste
D. Touch
E. Smell

_____8.   The underlined words in the following line are an example of which figurative device?

(Benedick; Act II, scene i)

ﾞﾑ

I cannot endure my *Lady Tongue!*

ﾞﾑ

A. Simile
B. Metaphor
C. Symbol
D. Personification
E. Irony

195

____9.   Which senses do the following lines appeal to?

(Benedick deriding Balthazar's love song; Act II, scene iii)

ða

An he had been a dog that should have howled thus, they would have hanged him: and I pray God his bad voice bode no mischief.

ða

A. Sight
B. Sound
C. Smell
D. Taste
E. Touch

____10.   The underlined words in the following line are an example of which figurative device?

(Claudio refusing Hero; Act IV, scene i)

ða

Give not this <u>rotten orange to your friend</u>.

ða

A. Simile
B. Metaphor
C. Symbol
D. Apostrophe
E. Irony

Postreading Activity
for
A Midsummer's Night's Dream
Vocabulary in Context
Act V

Directions: In each of the passages below you will find one of the words from the prereading vocabulary list for Act V. Review the definitions given in the prereading vocabulary. Working individually, in pairs, or in small groups as your teacher directs, examine each of the underlined words in the following passages from Act V. For each word, use the appropriate meaning and develop a brief interpretation of the passage within the context of the play.

1. Leonato decrying the denouncement of Hero (Act V, scene i):

    ઙ

    No, no; 'tis all men's office to speak patience
    To those that wring under the load of sorrow,
    But no man's virtue nor sufficiency
    To be so moral when he shall endure
    The like himself. Therefore give me no counsel:
    My griefs cry louder than <u>advertisement</u>.

    ઙ

2. Leonato trying to start a fight with Claudio and Don Pedro (Act V, scene i):

    ઙ

    Marry, thou dost wrong me; thou <u>dissembler</u>, thou!
    Nay, never lay thy hand upon thy sword;
    I fear thee not.

    ઙ

3. Antonio insulting Claudio and trying to pick a fight with him (Act V, scene i):

    ᕶ

    > *He shall kill two of us, and men indeed:*
    > *But that's no matter; let him kill one first;*
    > *Win me and wear me; let him answer me.*
    > *Come, follow me, boy; come, sir boy, come, follow me:*
    > *Sir boy, I'll whip you from your <u>foining</u> fence;*
    > *Nay, as I am a gentleman, I will.*

    ᕶ

4. A repentant Claudio asking Leonato's mercy for denouncing Hero falsely (Act V, scene i):

    ᕶ

    > *Choose your revenge yourself;*
    > *Impose me to what penance your <u>invention</u>*
    > *Can lay upon my sin: yet sinn'd I not*
    > *But in mistaking.*

    ᕶ

5. Antonio pretending to be the father of the bride (Act V, scene iv):

    ᕶ

    > *Which I will do with confirm'd <u>countenance</u>.*

    ᕶ

NAME: _____   DATE: _____

Vocabulary Review Quiz
for
Much Ado About Nothing
Act V

Directions: For each of the italicized words in the sentences below, determine which letter best reflects the use of the word in this context. Place the letter corresponding to your answer in the space to the left of the item number.

____1. When Leonato speaks of the *advertisement* of Hero's denunciation, he means

A. news stories of event.
B. posters of event.
C. knowledge of event.
D. paid advertising.
E. commercials.

____2. For Leonato to apply *dissembler* to the characters of Don Pedro and Claudio means that he views them as

A. villains.
B. hypocrites.
C. friends.
D. enemies.
E. kinsmen.

____3. When Antonio speaks of Claudio's *foining fence*, he is attempting to

A. praise his swordsmanship.
B. discredit his character.
C. accuse him of stealing.
D. belittle his swordsmanship.
E. vent his own anger.

____4. For Claudio to submit to the penance of Leonato's *invention* means

A. false penance.
B. whatever punishment Leonato conceives.
C. lawful punishment.
D. to praise Hero's memory.
E. to admit Claudio's mistake.

_____5.   When Antonio says he will perform the role of father of the bride with *confirm'd countenance*, he means that he will

   A. laugh out loud.
   B. pretend seriousness.
   C. wear a frown.
   D. have to be forced.
   E. refuse unless paid.

EXTENDING ACTIVITIES

Overview of
Extending Activities
for
Much Ado About Nothing

Directions: Now that you've completed your formal study of *Much Ado About Nothing*, the extending activities listed below will provide you with opportunities to extend your understanding of the play. Remember that these are suggestions of things you might do. Perhaps you will think of others or your teacher may have additional suggestions. Your teacher can provide you with specific sets of directions for *acting out, oral interpretation, puppet theater, masks, writing assignments, and visual displays.*

Acting Out

1. Dramatize a missing scene related to the characters and situations in the play. For example, in the stage version of the play we don't see Margaret impersonate Hero and call to Borachio, although in Branagh's film version we do. We also don't see the Sexton actually tell Leonato about Borachio's confession.

2. Present a scene from the play in a modern context. Use contemporary settings, words, and ideas. For example, what might Claudio's denunciation of Hero sound like in contemporary language?

Oral Interpretation   Present a prepared reading of the speech of a single character, between two characters, or of an entire scene. Keep in mind that oral interpretation involves communicating the words effectively *without* actually memorizing a script and acting out the scene with full costumes and props.

Puppetry and Masks

1. Make paper bag puppets and use them to present a scene from the play.

2. Create paper plate masks for specific characters and present a scene from the play using them.

Writing Assignments

1. Write an alternative ending to the play. What might happen if Hero actually had died and Claudio has to marry Antonio's ugly daughter? What do you think the wedding between Benedick and Beatrice will be like?

2. Research some element of English life at the time the play was written and performed (approximately 1600 A.D.)

3. Using the character diary you kept while reading the play, write a letter or note from your character to another character in the play or to a relative in a neighboring country.

Visual Displays

1. Create a graffiti wall for the City of Messina or Barcelona, the capital of Arragon, that reflects a specific time during the play.

2. Draw a comic strip or drawing for a scene from the play.

3. Create a filmstrip or video related to the play.

4. Construct a mobile using double-sided objects/characters from the play with a 3×5 card containing a description beneath each object.

5. Create a music video combining still pictures with music and words.

6. Select and depict 12 or 16 scenes from the play for a multiple panel quilt. Make each panel out of paper. For each panel of your quilt, create an illustration and write a caption that explains it. Create a border for each panel and tie or string them together using clothesline or heavy string to form a large wall hanging.

7. Research and build a Globe Theater model.

8. Report on the progress of the reconstruction of the Globe Theater in modern London.

9. Create a slide sound presentation on some aspect of the play.

Extending Activity
for
Much Ado About Nothing
Acting Out

Directions: From time to time during your study of *Much Ado About Nothing*, you may have participated in an improvised scene from the play either before or after you read particular scenes. Now that you've read the entire play, here are some additional opportunities for you to act out and demonstrate your fuller understanding of the play and its characters. You may wish to improvise these scenes or to fully script and rehearse them.

1. Suppose you were the servant who overheard Claudio and Don Pedro discussing the winning of Hero in Act I, scene i. How do you tell Antonio about Don Pedro wanting to woo Hero?

2. Suppose Ursula doesn't interrupt the verbal spat that Beatrice and Benedick have in Act V, scene ii. Just how far do you think these two would go?

3. After Don John is caught and returned to Don Pedro, what does he say?

4. If Don John, Borachio, and Conrade were to stand trial, what would they say for themselves?

5. Develop a segment for "60 Minutes," CBS Evening News (NBC or ABC), "Entertainment Tonight," "Oprah," "Geraldo," "Now It Can Be Told," or "A Current Affair" based upon *Much Ado About Nothing*.

Extending Activity
for
Much Ado About Nothing
Oral Interpretation

Directions: Present a prepared reading of a speech or scene from *Much Ado About Nothing*. Listed below are suggestions of scenes for one, two, or three or more actors to choose from. You may wish to check with your teacher and present other scenes.

To help you prepare your scene, work through all the steps.

One-Actor Scenes

Beatrice deriding Benedick's character (Act I, scene i)

Benedick's complaining about how Beatrice abused him at the ball (Act II, scene i)

Benedick contemplating how he might consider marriage (Act II, scene iii)

Benedick's response to overhearing the other men talk about Beatrice being hopelessly in love with Benedick (Act II, scene iii)

Beatrice overhearing Hero and Ursula (Act III, scene i)

Claudio's denunciation of Hero (Act IV, scene i)

Dogberry's examination of Borachio and Conrade (Act V, scene ii)

Claudio's epitaph (Act V, scene iii)

Two-Actor Scenes

Beatrice and Benedick confront each other (Act I, scene i)

Claudio and Benedick discuss Hero (Act I, scene i)

Claudio asks Don Pedro to woo Hero (Act I, scene i)

Leonato and Beatrice discuss the perfect man (Act II, scene i)

Benedick and Beatrice feud during the ball (Act II, scene i)

Don John and Borachio discuss their plan to discredit Hero (Act II, scene ii)

Benedick professes his love to Beatrice (Act IV, scene i)

Benedick woos Beatrice (Act V, scene ii)

*Scenes for Three or
More Actors*

Benedick disdains marriage to Don Pedro and Claudio (Act I, scene i)

Don Pedro informs Benedick and Claudio that he has won Hero for Claudio (Act II, scene i)

Don Pedro, Leonato, and Claudio convince Benedick that Beatrice loves him (Act II, scene iii)

Hero, Margaret, and Ursula convince Beatrice that Benedick loves her (Act III, scene ii)

Don Pedro, Claudio, and Leonato tease Benedick about being in love (Act III, scene ii)

Hero, Margaret, Ursula, and Beatrice prepare for the wedding (Act III, scene iv)

Claudio denounces Hero (Act IV, scene i)

Dogberry conducts the examination (Act V, scene ii)

Claudio marries Leonato's "niece" (Act V, scene iv)

*Steps for
Preparing an
Oral Interpretation*

1. Select a scene or passage that you really like. The passage should have a definite beginning, high point, and an end. Remember that you will be doing a prepared reading and not memorizing a script. Most often oral interpreters either stand before their audience or sit on a stool.

2. Prepare a script to work from. You may wish to type out the selection or copy it from a book. You'll need a copy that you can make notes on. Mount your script on black construction paper, so you can read from it easily without having to hold it with both hands. Keep the pages of your manuscript loose, so you can either slide them out of the way or shift them under each other as you finish reading them.

3. Analyze the script. As you work through the analysis, make notes to yourself in pencil on your script.

    a. Read the whole passage and decide what it's about. Because you've already read the whole play, you know where your selection fits into the development of the characters.

    b. Read the whole piece several times and decide what the overall effect of the piece is.

    c.   Make notes of things you don't understand, such as allusions, words, and so forth. Check the footnotes in your text or look up unfamiliar words in the dictionary. Remember that the meaning of particular words may have changed since Shakespeare's time. If you have a problem understanding a particular word, check the glossary of terms found in most *Complete Works of Shakespeare* in your library.

    d.   As you look at individual words, you should know how to pronounce all of them as well as know both their denotative meaning (the dictionary meaning) and their connotative meaning (the emotional subtleties that come from using the word in a particular context).

    e.   Where does the scene take place? Is it within the house or in the garden?

    f.   Examine the overall organization of the scene. What emotions do the characters reveal in this scene? What changes in character, motivation, or emotions occur during the scene? How does the mood change from joy to sorrow in Act IV, scene i where Claudio denounces Hero?

4.   Begin practicing aloud. Read the passage out loud, working either with a partner or with a tape recorder. Listen to yourself. Experiment with different readings. Underline words you wish to emphasize. Make marginal notes about the emotions you wish to portray in different parts.

5.   Write a brief introduction to your scene, setting it up for your listeners. The following example could be used to introduce Act IV, scene i:

The shy but brave soldier Claudio has won Leonato's daughter Hero through the intervention of Don Pedro, Prince of Arragon. However, Borachio, one of Don John's henchmen, has tricked Claudio into believing that Hero is unfaithful. Borachio had Margaret, one of Hero's handmaids, dress in Hero's clothes and call fondly to Borachio from Hero's window while Claudio, Don Pedro, and Don John watched. At the wedding, Claudio denounces Hero publicly.

6.   Once you've decided how you wish to read your selection, practice, practice, practice! Your goal in these sessions is not to memorize the words but to learn the interpretation, so that when you present it, you can concentrate on a smooth performance.

7.   Perform the piece. Some interpreters prefer to stand while others prefer to sit upon stools. You may hold the script in your hands or use a music stand or lectern.

NAME: _____   DATE: _____

Extending Activity
for
Much Ado About Nothing
Puppet Theater

One way to present scenes from *Much Ado About Nothing* without having to worry about elaborate sets or costumes is to use puppets made from brown paper bags. You can make your own puppets using construction paper, scissors, rubber cement, crayons, and felt-tip markers. You can use a table turned sideways as a stage for the puppeteers to hide behind. If you feel that you need scenery, make a mural and use masking tape to secure it to the wall behind you.

Steps to Making and Performing Scene with Puppets:

1. Select a scene that you want to perform. Listed below are scenes for two, and three or more actors.

*Scenes for
Two Actors*

Beatrice and Benedick confront each other (Act I, scene i)

Claudio and Benedick discuss Hero (Act I, scene i)

Claudio asks Don Pedro to woo Hero (Act I, scene i)

Leonato and Beatrice discuss the perfect man (Act II, scene i)

Benedick and Beatrice feud during the ball (Act II, scene i)

Don John and Borachio discuss their plan to discredit Hero (Act II, scene ii)

Benedick professes his love to Beatrice (Act IV, scene i)

Benedick woos Beatrice (Act V, scene ii)

*Scenes for
Three or
More Actors*

Benedick disdains marriage to Don Pedro and Claudio (Act I, scene i)

Don Pedro informs Benedick and Claudio that he has won Hero for Claudio (Act II, scene i)

Don Pedro, Leonato, and Claudio convince Benedick that Beatrice loves him (Act II, scene iii)

Hero, Margaret, and Ursula convince Beatrice that Benedick loves her (Act III, scene ii)

Don Pedro, Claudio, and Leonato tease Benedick about being in love (Act III, scene ii)

Hero, Margaret, Ursula, and Beatrice prepare for the wedding (Act III, scene iv)

Claudio denounces Hero (Act IV, scene i)

Dogberry conducts the examination (Act V, scene ii)

Claudio marries Leonato's niece (Act V, scene iv)

2. Design and make puppets. In making your puppets, refer to **Figure 1**. To make your puppet talk, insert your hand into the bag and curl your fingers so the upper face on the top of the bag moves up and down.

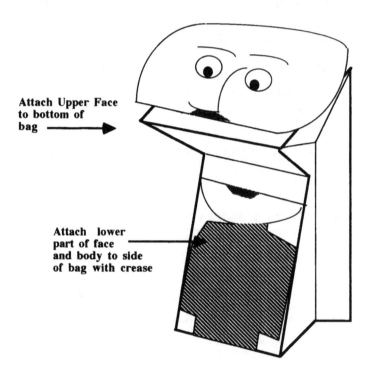

Figure 1
Paper Bag Puppet

3. Prepare your script as if you were doing an oral interpretation. See specific directions entitled "Extending Activity for *Much Ado About Nothing*: Oral Interpretation."

4. Decide how you can make your puppet appear to walk and move.

5. Practice, practice, practice.

Extending Activity
for
Much Ado About Nothing
Paper Plate Masks

Directions: One way to help you present scenes from *Much Ado About Nothing* is to create a half mask to represent the character in a specific scene. When you present your scene, hold the mask in front of you to create the character. To make your own mask, you will need:

large white paper plates (do not use plastic plates)

large craft stick

scissors

glue (either rubber cement or hot melt glue gun work well)

assorted construction paper, ribbon, cloth, cardboard, yarn to make hair, hats and other decorations that help represent the character

crayons, colored pencils, or felt-tip markers

Assemble the mask as illustrated in **Figure 2**.

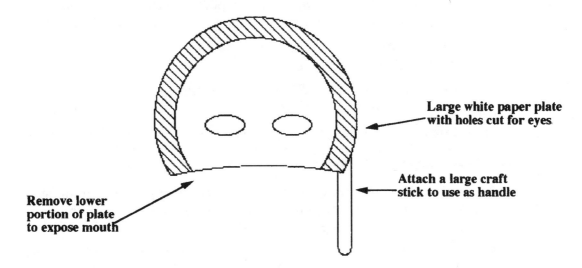

Large white paper plate with holes cut for eyes

Attach a large craft stick to use as handle

Remove lower portion of plate to expose mouth

Figure 2
Paper Plate Mask

You may wish to draw or paint directly on the plate or use construction paper.

Extending Activity
for
Much Ado About Nothing
Writing Assignments

Directions: Given below are some ideas for possible writing assignments based on your understanding of the characters and situations in *Much Ado About Nothing*.

1. You are the casting director for a new rock version of *Much Ado About Nothing*. Write a letter to the film's producers explaining whom from among current film, television, or rock and roll stars you would like to cast in each of the play's principal roles: Benedick, Beatrice, Hero, Claudio, Don Pedro, Don John, Dogberry.

2. Write a modern version of Claudio's epitaph for Hero.

3. Write a new or more satisfying ending to the play.

4. Create a "Meeting of Minds" where characters from *Much Ado About Nothing* interact with characters from other literature. You may also want to have the characters interact with their authors.

5. Create a children's version of the play. Check *Shake Hands with Shakespeare* or Charles and Caroline Lamb's *Tales from Shakespeare*.

6. Create an illustrated children's book or animated version based upon *Much Ado About Nothing*.

7. Investigate the Globe Theater restoration project in London and report your findings to the class.

8. Research the food, clothing, housing, festivals, or celebrations for either Elizabethan England at the time of *Much Ado About Nothing* (approximately 1600 A.D.).

9. Using the character diary that you kept during your reading of the play, write a letter to your cousin in London relaying both the events of the play and your response to them.

10. As one of the characters in the play, write a letter to either "Dear Abby" or "Ann Landers" and imagine the columnist's reply.

PART THREE

Appendices

Appendix A

EVALUATING READING PROCESS ACTIVITIES

This section will show you how to evaluate and assign grades for reading process activities for a unit on *Much Ado About Nothing*, and how to set up and review reading activity folders. It also reviews the instructional goals for all activities and suggests specific guidelines for evaluating them.

ASSESSING STUDENTS' PARTICIPATION

With a reading workshop approach to literature, just as with a writing workshop approach to written composition, you must decide how to assess students' participation in process activities and to evaluate the formal products that demonstrate learning as well. The activities in this resource provide opportunities for students to improve their reading, writing, speaking, listening, and critical thinking processes as well as learn about *Much Ado About Nothing*. Although you don't need to grade all the process activities formally, you will want to review and respond to your students' work as they read the play. If you and your students were to devote approximately two to three weeks to a unit on *Much Ado About Nothing*, you might use the percentages listed in the table below.

SUGGESTED COMPONENTS OF UNIT GRADE

Activity	Percentage of Unit Grade	Numbers of Items and Point Values	Total
		(Intro with videotape and 4	
Prereading activities	5%	other reading sessions @ 5 pts.)	25 pts.
Response journals or character diaries	25%	(5 [one per act] @ 20 pts.)	125 pts.
Postreading activities	10%	(5 summary sessions @ 10 pts.)	50 pts.
Comprehension checks	10%	(5 @ 10 pts.)	50 pts.
Vocabulary review quizzes	10%	(5 @ 10 pts.)	50 pts.
Language exploration activities	10%	(5 @ 10 pts.)	50 pts.
Language exploration review quiz	5%		25 pts.
Individual or group extending activity	25%		125 pts.
Total	**100%**		**500 pts.**

SETTING UP AND REVIEWING READING ACTIVITY FOLDERS

Reading folders allow the students to keep their prereading, during-reading, and postreading activities together for the entire unit. Any type of folder works well, although two pocket folders allow students to store their response journals or character diaries on one side and other reading process activities on the other.

To monitor students' progress and to provide formative evaluation, review approximately 20 percent of the students' folders for each class period at the end of each day. Select the folders at random, so individual students won't know when you will check any individual's work. Take a few minutes to skim and scan the work in each folder.

As you review each student's work, check to see that the student understands the directions and purpose of each activity. Use brief comments to praise the work specifically and to point out specific deficiencies. Then record the date of your review and any point values. You might try using + ✓ for outstanding work, ✓ for satisfactory work, and − ✓ for less than satisfactory work because students may find these symbols less threatening than traditional letter grades. You can translate codes like these into a numerical equivalent for your records: for example, awarding 5 points for outstanding work, 4 for satisfactory, and 3 for less than satisfactory.

INSTRUCTIONAL GOALS AND EVALUATIVE GUIDELINES FOR SPECIFIC READING ACTIVITIES

This section states both the instructional goals for specific reading process activities and suggests means to assess them.

Focusing Activities

Although students complete only *one* focusing activity for a particular scene, all focusing activities share two common *instructional goals*:

- ❧ to organize students' prior knowledge related to *Much Ado About Nothing*
- ❧ to establish a purpose for reading a scene

Scenarios for Improvisation

Guidelines for Assessment

Does the student

- ❧ participate actively as either actor or audience?
- ❧ provide logical motivations for character's actions?
- ❧ establish actions that are consistent with setting and existing information about character?

Prereading Discussion Questions

Guidelines for Assessment:

Does the student

- ❧ participate in discussion?
- ❧ share ideas willingly?

- allow others to share ideas?
- provide explanation or support for ideas?
- provide speculations that are consistent with the student's existing knowledge of *Much Ado About Nothing*?

Speculation Journal

Guidelines for Assessment:
   Does the student

- address the issues contained in the question(s)?
- provide explanation or support for ideas?
- provide speculations that are consistent with the student's existing knowledge of *Much Ado About Nothing*?

Introducing the Play With Videotape

Guidelines for Assessment:
   Does the student

- attempt to answer all the questions?
- address the issues in the prompt?
- have an overall understanding of the scene and its conflict?

Vocabulary

Instructional Goals:
- to review definitions of less familiar words
- to demonstrate the effect of context upon meaning

Plot Summaries

Instructional Goals:
- to establish an overview of each scene
- to provide a reference for the student when Shakespeare's text seems incomprehensible

Response Journals

As one of two on-going writing-to-learn activities that students may use during their reading of *Much Ado About Nothing*, the response journal has two *instructional goals*:

- to summarize and reflect upon the meaning of the play

❧ to recognize, record, and comment upon repeated elements found in the play, such as symbols, motifs, themes, character development, or figurative language

Guidelines for Assessment:

Does the student

❧ record an entry for each reading session and each scene within it?

❧ meet minimum length requirements for each entry?

❧ respond emotionally, associatively, figuratively?

❧ demonstrate an accurate understanding of the literary facts of *Much Ado About Nothing*?

❧ demonstrate an honest effort to begin making sense of the play and developing an understanding of it?

❧ probe responses and attempt to understand them rather than only summarize or paraphrase the action of the play?

Character Diary

As one of two on-going writing-to-learn activities that students may use during their reading of *Much Ado About Nothing*, the character diary has two *instructional goals*:

❧ to summarize and reflect upon the meaning of the play

❧ to begin to evaluate the action of the play from the perspective of an individual character

Guidelines for Assessment:

Does the student

❧ record an entry for each reading session?

❧ meet minimum length requirements for each entry?

❧ provide an account for how the character learns of the action of the scene(s) just read?

❧ demonstrate an accurate understanding of the literary facts of *Much Ado About Nothing*?

❧ demonstrate an honest effort to begin making sense of the play and developing an understanding of it?

❧ probe responses and attempt to understand them rather than only summarize or paraphrase the action of the play?

Viewing a Scene on Videotape

Unlike using a scene to introduce *Much Ado About Nothing*, viewing a scene after students have read it provides additional information that may help them to understand the text of the play.

Instructional Goals:

- to recognize that the performance of a scene affects the student's understanding, comprehension, and interpretation of it

- to compare and contrast a student's interpretation of a scene with the performers'

Guidelines for Assessment:

Does the student

- attempt to answer all the questions?

- address the issues in the questions?

- demonstrate an honest effort to make sense of the presentation?

- begin to make connections between the videotaped presentation and the text of *Much Ado About Nothing*?

Guides to Character Development

Although students complete these activities after they've read each act, they will reread and contemplate specific portions of the play actively. The students may examine Beatrice, Benedick, Claudio, and Hero as major characters; Don Pedro, Leonato, Margaret, Borachio, Don John, and Dogberry as minor ones.

Instructional Goals:

- to recognize and identify means that Shakespeare uses to develop or reveal character

- to use evidence from the play to develop and support an interpretation of a character

Guidelines for Assessment:

Does the student

- attempt to answer all the questions?

- address the issues in the questions?

- use information from the play to develop and support logical conclusions about character(s)?

Comprehension Checks

Both the Comprehension Check and the Small Group Discussion Questions provide means for assessing each student's reading comprehension.

Comprehension Checks (multiple choice)

Instructional Goal:

- ❦ to assess reading comprehension of an entire act through factual, interpretative, and evaluative questions

Guideline for Assessment:

- ❦ answer keys appear in Appendix C

Small Group Discussion Questions

Instructional Goal:

- ❦ to assess reading comprehension of an entire act through factual, interpretative, and evaluative questions

Guidelines for Assessment:

Does the student

- ❦ participate in discussion?
- ❦ attempt to answer all the questions?
- ❦ address the issues in the questions?
- ❦ use information from the play to develop and support logical conclusions about the play?

Critical Thinking Questions

Instructional Goals:

- ❦ to connect the play to the student's life in meaningful ways
- ❦ to evaluate interpretations of the play using textual evidence, personal experience, and knowledge of related literature

Guidelines for Assessment:

Does the student

- ❦ attempt to answer both the exploration questions as well as the focus question?
- ❦ address the issues of each question appropriately?
- ❦ use specific information to support ideas?
- ❦ integrate personal experience, knowledge of related literature, and textual evidence?
- ❦ draw logical conclusions from the existing evidence?

Language Exploration Activities

Instructional Goals:

- ❧ to review definitions of selected literary devices and examine them within the context of *Much Ado About Nothing*
- ❧ to apply knowledge of literary devices with textual evidence to develop and evaluate interpretations of specific passages of *Much Ado About Nothing*

Guidelines for Assessment:

Suggested answers appear in Appendix C.
Does the student

- ❧ complete the items that the teacher assigns?
- ❧ make an effort to apply the definition of the literary device to the lines in the play?
- ❧ review the passage within the broader context of the individual speech, scene, or play?
- ❧ provide specific support of interpretation(s)?

Language Exploration Review Quiz

Instructional Goal:

- ❧ to assess student's understanding of how specific literary devices affect the interpretation of specific passages from *Much Ado About Nothing*

Guidelines for Assessment:

Suggested answers appear in Appendix C.
Has the student

- ❧ completed the preceding language exploration activities?

Vocabulary in Context

Instructional Goals:

- ❧ to review the additional meanings of words
- ❧ to analyze the use of specific words within the context of a particular passage
- ❧ to develop interpretations of specific passages using knowledge and context

Guidelines for Assessment:

Suggested answers appear in Appendix C.
Does the student

- ❧ complete the items that the teacher assigns?
- ❧ review the definitions of the words?
- ❧ make an effort to apply the meaning of the word to the lines in the play?

- ⁊ review the passage within the broader context of the individual speech, scene, or play?
- ⁊ provide specific support of interpretation(s)?

Vocabulary Review Quizzes

Instructional Goal:

- ⁊ to assess student's understanding of specific words in context

Guidelines for Assessment:

Suggested answers appear in Appendix C.
Has the student

- ⁊ reviewed the meaning of the words?
- ⁊ completed the preceding vocabulary in context activities?

Individual or Group Extending Activities

Instructional Goals:

- ⁊ to apply knowledge and understanding of *Much Ado About Nothing* to new situations and contexts
- ⁊ to provide additional opportunities for students to apply reading, writing, speaking, listening, viewing, and critical thinking skills

Guidelines for Assessment:

Does the student

- ⁊ have a purpose and focus for the extending activity that is related to the play and the study of it directly?
- ⁊ present information clearly and logically?
- ⁊ present information, whether from the play or research, accurately and with appropriate documentation?
- ⁊ present interpretations of characters or events from the play that are consistent with the information in the text?
- ⁊ meet all appropriate additional criteria and specifications that the teacher sets?

Appendix B

USING SMALL GROUPS SUCCESSFULLY

I advocate using small groups throughout this resource. Small groups are a great way to get lots of students involved quickly. Several practices make these groups operate more effectively:

- ﷼ Assign students to specific groups. When students self-select their groups, they may socialize rather than focus on the task at hand.

- ﷼ Mix students of different backgrounds, abilities, and talents. In discussion situations, multiple perspectives often lead to insights.

- ﷼ Structure the group assignments and provide written directions (on the chalkboard, overhead projector, or in written handouts). When students know their audience and the purpose of the assignment, they tend to stay on task. All members of the group need to understand what their jobs are, what the final product needs to look like, and how much time they have to complete it.

- ﷼ Establish class rules for small group behavior and encourage students to work together.

- ﷼ Monitor students' behavior as they work in groups. Move around the room in a random fashion.

Appendix C

ANSWER KEYS

COMPREHENSION CHECKS

Act I			Act II			Act III	
1.	B		1.	E		1.	B
2.	C		2.	B		2.	C
3.	A		3.	D		3.	C
4.	B		4.	D		4.	C
5.	A		5.	A		5.	A

Act IV			Act V	
1.	C		1.	D
2.	C		2.	D
3.	C		3.	B
4.	D		4.	C
5.	D		5.	A

SUGGESTED ANSWERS TO
SMALL GROUP DISCUSSION QUESTIONS

Act I

1. According to what Leonato tells the messenger, there has been a running verbal feud between Benedick and Beatrice for some time. Beatrice demonstrates her verbal wit for the audience even before we see Benedick.

2. Although Claudio is an accomplished soldier, he doesn't see himself as a person experienced in the game of courtly love as is Don Pedro. He has found his feelings toward Hero have changed to love since he returned from war.

3. As Don Pedro's governor of Messina, Leonato could expect Don Pedro to approach him directly prior to wooing Hero. This also suggests that Leonato has noticed that Hero seems quite taken by Claudio.

4. Don John is an archetypal villain, so he really doesn't need much motive. However, as Don Pedro's illegitimate half-brother, he apparently has mounted a rebellion against Don Pedro that failed. It's from this war that Don Pedro and the others are returning. In addition to being defeated, Don John has also been reconciled with his brother.

Act II

1. The ideal man would have half of Benedick's talkative nature, half of Don John's melancholy, a good leg and foot, and enough money.

2. Don Pedro and Hero engage in courtly love, for Hero believes that Don Pedro is Claudio. Ursula and Antonio flirt. Margaret and Borachio engage in earthy humor.

3. Borachio's plan is to have Claudio, Don Pedro, and Don John witness Margaret (disguised as Hero) call to Borachio as a lover would from her window on the eve of her wedding to Claudio, thereby compromising her reputation.

4. Benedick is convinced by Leonato's word.

5. The exchange between Benedick and Beatrice at the end of the act reflects the same relationship we've seen before; however, Benedick sees it as proof that Beatrice loves him.

Act III

1. Hero and Ursula become more exaggerated in their language and make sure they can be overheard. They also make asides to each other about how well their plan is working.

2. Beatrice has a brief soliloquy at the end of the scene, showing that she's understood what Hero and Ursula have said. She also vows to requite Benedick's love.

3. Again, they too resort to exaggeration and exchanges to indicate they know their trick is working.

4. The men kid Benedick rather mercilessly. Once Don John enters, the tone turns quite somber.

5. Because Beatrice is a renowned wit, she sees the pun in Cardus Benedictus (a reference to Benedick being the cure for what ails Beatrice) that Margaret does not.

Act IV

1. Claudio becomes less courteous and more direct as he accuses Hero. Leonato goes from disbelief to accusing Hero himself. A large portion of this scene is in blank verse.

2. Comparisons Claudio uses are rotten fruit and acting as a pagan animal.

3. The Friar suggests that Hero pretend to be dead until her reputation can be restored.

4. Although Benedick professes his love for Beatrice, she goads him into promising to kill Claudio.

5. Dogberry doesn't even seem to know how to conduct an examination. The Sexton has to prompt him as to what to do. It is the Sexton who realizes that what the men are accused of has already come to pass that morning.

Act V

1. The Prince and Claudio don't fight Leonato and Antonio out of respect for their age. They don't believe at first that Benedick is serious.

2. Claudio wishes to atone for the death of his beloved Hero and help to restore her reputation.

3. In spite of trying to act much more like Claudio and Hero, these two can't resist the opportunity for a verbal battle.

4. The masks convey a somberness and mystery.

5. The wedding in Act IV begins happily and ends in sorrow. The wedding in Act V reverses the sequence.

SUGGESTED ANSWERS FOR LANGUAGE EXPLORATION ACTIVITIES

Act I: Simile and Metaphor

1. The metaphor compares Claudio to a lion in terms of valor, to a lamb because of his youth.

2. The simile compares Benedick's faith to the fashion of a hat that changes with each blocking.

3. Beatrice's simile compares Benedick to a disease.

4. In this subsequent metaphor, Benedick becomes the disease whose cure is to spend a friend's money.

5. Indirectly, Beatrice's metaphor compares men in love to dogs.

6. Claudio's metaphor compares Hero to a rare jewel.

7. The simile compares how much more beautiful Beatrice is than Hero: May is more beautiful than December.

8. Here Benedick compares marriage to being yoked like an ox.

9. The simile compares love-struck Benedick with a cat.

10. Claudio's metaphor here places his emotions within the rooms of a house.

Act II: Personification

1. Benedick makes the act of courtesy a traitor or turncoat.
2. Repentance is an old man on bad legs who can't dance.
3. Here Ursula suggests that Antonio personifies virtue.
4. Friendship is a constant in all except politics and love.
5. Hearts in love have tongues.
6. Eyes can negotiate and not trust intermediaries.
7. Beauty is a witch.
8. A dying oak would have answered Beatrice.
9. The mask began to scold her.
10. Silence is a herald.

Act III: Sensory Imagery

1. These references are to eating: taste and smell.
2. Benedick's comparison appeals to sight.
3. Beatrice refers to both touch and sight.
4. These images appeal to sight.
5. The muzzle can be seen and often stifles a growl (hearing); biting is touch.
6. These can be seen and the money heard as well.
7. These are comic sights.
8. Generally appeals to sight although a garland of flowers would also smell.
9. These images appeal to sight.
10. These images appeal to sight.

Act IV: Apostrophe

1. According to the men, Beatrice addresses an absent Benedick in her rooms.
2. Beatrice addresses the absent Benedick.
3. All three of the men address abstract qualities as though present and active: the day, mischief, a plague.
4. Claudio appeals to authority.
5. Leonato uses apostrophes addressing both fate and death.

Act V: Symbol

1. The man in marriage is a yoked ox.

2. The image suggests that Cupid has spent all his arrows on the population of Venice; Venice is a city renowned for love or prostitution.

3. Claudio is the schoolboy in his innocence; Hero is the bird's nest; and because Claudio believes that Don Pedro has stolen Hero, Don Pedro is the companion.

4. Benedick wouldn't marry Beatrice if she had all the wealth of the Garden of Eden.

5. Beatrice sees a marriage to the head of state as being too fancy for her to wear every day.

LANGUAGE EXPLORATION REVIEW QUIZ

1. B
2. A
3. B
4. C
5. E
6. A
7. E
8. D
9. B
10. A

SUGGESTED ANSWERS FOR VOCABULARY IN CONTEXT

With all these exercises, encourage students to discuss their ideas and interpretations, for their answers will vary. These are suggestions and shouldn't be interpreted as the only valid responses.

Act I

1. Beatrice belittles Benedick as a fool who claims to be able to vouch for Cupid.

2. Here Leonato mentions the on-going war of words between the two.

3. A squarer is a quarreler.

4. A continuer is one who persists in behaving the same way. He's also suggesting that Beatrice is horse-like; a nag perhaps?

5. Beatrice uses a common scornful term here: jade, a broken-down horse. She's saying that Benedick didn't end fairly.

6. Claudio fears that he may be entrapped.

7. Don Pedro suggests that ultimately, with time, Benedick will come to marry.

8. Here, once means once for all.

9. The event is an occurrence, a result.

10. As used here, inform.

Act II

1. Beatrice has a shrewish, scolding tongue.

2. Antonio claims to mimic or imitate himself.

3. Honorably.

4. Abuse through words.

5. Put or turned aside.

Act III

1. Pleaching is a decorative interweaving of vines or branches.

2. In this case, evidence.

3. Obscured by smoke or vapor.

4. Smudged.

5. Comprehension or understanding.

Act IV

1. Leonato urges the Friar to wait until after the ceremony to instruct the couple in their personal or private duties as husband and wife.

2. Claudio suggests a gift to counterbalance Hero.

3. Claudio calls Hero a wanton or wild person.

4. Abuse.

5. Claudio will forever be skeptical of Hero.

Act V

1. General knowledge or gossip.
2. Hypocrite.
3. Thrusting or slashing with a sharp object.
4. Imagination.
5. Face.

VOCABULARY REVIEW QUIZZES

Act I		Act II		Act III		Act IV		Act V	
1.	C	1.	C	1.	C	1.	B	1.	C
2.	A	2.	A	2.	C	2.	E	2.	B
3.	C	3.	B	3.	C	3.	B	3.	D
4.	B	4.	C	4.	E	4.	C	4.	B
5.	B	5.	C	5.	B	5.	B	5.	B
6.	C								
7.	A								
8.	D								
9.	D								
10.	D								

Appendix D

BIBLIOGRAPHY

Abcarian, Richard and Marvin Klotz, eds. *Literature: The Human Experience*. rev., shorter ed. New York: St. Martin's, 1984.

Asimov, Isaac. *Asimov's Guide to Shakespeare: The Greek, Roman, and Italian Plays*. Vol. 1. Garden City: Doubleday, 1970.

Barnet, Sylvan, Morton Berman, and William Burto, eds. *An Introduction to Literature: Fiction, Poetry, Drama*. Glenview: Scott, Foresman, 1989.

Bleich, David. *Readings and Feelings: A Guide to Subjective Criticism*. Urbana: National Council of Teachers of English, 1975.

Brockett, Oscar G. *History of the Theatre*. Boston: Allyn and Bacon, 1968.

Brown, Hazel and Brian Cambourne. *Read and Retell: A Strategy for the Whole-Language/Natural Learning Classroom*. Portsmouth: Heinemann, 1987.

Cambourne, Brian. *The Whole Story: Natural Learning and the Acquisition of Literacy in the Classroom*. New York: Ashton-Scholastic, 1989.

Christenbury, Leila A. and Patricia P. Kelly. *Questioning: The Path to Critical Thinking*. ERIC/RCS Theory and Research into Practice (TRIP) Monograph Series. Urbana: NCTE, 1983.

The Complete Works of William Shakespeare: His Plays and Poetry (CD-ROM disk). Portland, OR: Creative Multimedia, 1992.

Davis, James E. and Ronald E. Salomone, eds. *Teaching Shakespeare Today*. Urbana: NCTE, 1993.

Fox, Levi. *William Shakespeare: A Concise Life*. Norwich, England: Jerrold Printing, 1991.

Lee, Charlotte and David Grote. *Theater: Preparation and Performance*. Glenview: Scott, Foresman, 1982.

Miller, Bruce E. *Teaching the Art of Literature*. Urbana: National Council of Teachers of English, 1980.

Robinson, Randal. *Unlocking Shakespeare's Language*. ERIC/RCS Theory and Research into Practice (TRIP) Monograph Series. Urbana: NCTE, 1989.

Much Ado About Nothing in *William Shakespeare: The Complete Works*. Charles Jasper Sisson, ed. New York: Harper & Row, 1953: 144-173.

Rygiel, Mary Ann. *Shakespeare Among Schoolchildren: Approaches for the Secondary Classroom*. Urbana: NCTE, 1992.

Stanford, Judith A. *Responding to Literature*. Mountain View: Mayfield Publishing, 1992.

Vaughn, Joseph L. and Thomas H. Estes. *Reading and Reasoning Beyond the Primary Grades*. Boston: Allyn and Bacon, 1986.

Wright, Louis B. and Virginia A. LaMar, eds. *The Folger Guide to Shakespeare*. New York: Washington Square Press, 1969.

Appendix E

VERSIONS OF *MUCH ADO ABOUT NOTHING*
AVAILABLE ON VIDEOTAPE

Much Ado About Nothing. (1984). BBC/PBS production for "Shakespeare Plays" series. Robert Lindsay and Cherie Lunghi. Color. 120 minutes.

Much Ado About Nothing. (1993). Kenneth Branagh's film production. Kenneth Branagh, Emma Thompson, Keanu Reeves, Michael Keaton, Denzel Washington. Color. 110 minutes.

Availability and Cost:

BBC/PBS versions are available through larger video rental chains, state or regional public libraries, or state or regional educational film/media service libraries. Check with your school's librarian or media specialist.

Cost to purchase these video versions range from $20–$100.

The Writing Company issues a special Shakespeare Catalog. Address: 10200 Jefferson Boulevard, Culver City, CA 90232.

Versions may also be available at Filmic Archives, The Cinema Center, Botsford, CT 06404 at 1-800-366-1920, or Films for the Humanities, P.O. Box 2053, Princeton, NJ 08543-2053 at 1-800-257-5126.

Notes

Notes

Notes

Notes